PRAISE FOR *Take a Larger Way*

In *Take a Larger Way,* Jay Brenneman unpacks the painful pivot from a husband/lover/companion with a bright future (Plan A) to an unprepared caregiver with an uncertain future (Plan B). Jay and Janene's love story is captured in a collection of beautiful essays, masterfully written and deeply moving. For all of us who have cared for a loved one with this dreadful disease, Jay's reflections will help put into words what we all experienced but could not articulate. In my 15-plus years of volunteer leadership with the Alzheimer's Association, this is the best caregiving testimony I have ever had the privilege of hearing. Soak in it. Ponder it. Smile and weep. You will be glad you did.

> — Christopher Binkley, former chairman, governing board, Alzheimer's Association, Chicago, 2017-2018. Former Regional President, Kaiser Permanente of Colorado and Georgia

We're all fortunate Jay had the foresight, or need, to journal as his wife slowly succumbed to Frontal Temporal Degeneration (FTD). Jay's journey through bereavement as he discovers his own humanity, and ultimately his own strength, is one we can all reflect upon as we make our way through a fraught world. He describes the unique, ambiguous circularity of the grief experienced by those who lose a loved one in an incremental way.

— Terencia Beauvais-Nikl, co-founder and
moderator of FTD support group Colorado

How can we prepare when the one we love develops dementia and begins slipping away? There are no answers to the questions that scream in our mind: why this person? what am I losing? what can I do? But there can be insight found in the journey of Jay Brenneman as he watches his lovely and accomplished Janene in her own struggle, joyously remembering and then completely forgetting him in the same conversation. His is an elegant and elegiac journey of loss. If this is happening to you, or to a friend, or to people you know, then insight comes when you walk a mile in the shoes of one who has been there.

— Barry Petersen, CBS News senior
correspondent. Best Selling Author of *Jan's Story:
Love Lost to the Long Goodbye of Alzheimer's*

Our culture resists descent and suffering, leaving us unpracticed and afraid. Jay Brenneman's reflections bring light into the darkness of a situation we cannot fix, control, or change, making sacred our wounds that are borne in loneliness and grief.

— Fr. Richard Rohr, Franciscan. Author, Founder
of The Center for Contemplation and Action

Take a Larger Way

Take a
LARGER
WAY

Reflections of a
Dementia Caregiver

JAY BRENNEMAN

RETELLING, LLC

ISBN 978-1-7369457-1-1

CLAUDE MONET PAINTING & DRAWING
COVER *Stacks of Wheat (Sunset, Snow Effect)*, 1891. The Art Institute of Chicago.
P.1 *Stacks of Wheat*, 1891. Art Institute of Chicago.

PUBLISHED IN ASSOCIATION WITH Retelling | retelling.net
COVER DESIGN BY Cynthia Young | youngdesign.biz

To Christine, Rachel, and Lisa,
my three daughters whose steadfast love
and untiring support make all the difference

CONTENTS

Claude Monet. *Stacks of Wheat*, 1891.
Art Institute of Chicago.

1 | MONET MOMENT

I HAVE LONG BEEN an unsophisticated art devotee of Monet's impressionistic work. So when the unrenowned Denver Art Museum collected 120 of his pieces from around the world and created an exhibit entitled *Claude Monet: The Truth of Nature*, it was a must for me. But with all my novice enthusiasm for touring the display of Monet's extraordinary gift, I was still not prepared for what turned out to be an unforgettable moment—an *anagnorisis*, that uncommon word describing the moment in a play or novel, usually a tragic one, when the main character discovers the true nature of his or her circumstances.

It was December 11, 2019, at 12:30 in the afternoon during an otherwise routine and deeply appreciative viewing of the artistic vision of the man who founded French Impressionistic painting. Along with a dear friend, I rounded a bend on the now memorable second floor of the exhibit when my eyes came to rest on three of Monet's "Haystack Series." I was instantly flooded with emotion.

This was no slight tearing up that a quick blink of the eye makes unobservable to those nearby. My whole body began to tremble. I eyed a museum bench close by and quickly sat in an attempt to collect myself and manage the wave of emotion.

And it was then I heard The Voice in a riveting line: "This is why you are writing."

As I processed this experience with my friend who had joined me at the museum, we recalled a phrase that had captured our imagination during the introduction to Monet's work. The exhibit explanation began with: "He is a master of the intangible."

I began to investigate what Monet's intention might have been in his artistic painting. What I came to discover was that no less than 25 of the artist's works were dedicated to the modest motif of grain stacks outside his farmhouse in Giverny. That afternoon on the second floor of the art museum, the editors of the book by the same title as the exhibit—*Claude Monet: The Truth of Nature*—began to shed some light on the experience and the quandary of meaning it presented to me.

> While his repeated rendering of one and the same motif may seem to have elevated the object itself to a special status, the canvas's consistent variations of color and light, as well as their representation at recognizably different seasons of the year, showed

that his primary interest was not the subject matter of grain stacks at all. Instead, he focused on
capturing the atmosphere that surrounded them
at any given time...[1]

The editors go on to report what Monet himself made
even more explicit about his mastery of the intangible when
he asserted that:

To me, the motif is something insignificant; what
I want to reproduce is what lies between the motif
and me. For me, a landscape hardly exists at all as
a landscape, because its appearance is constantly
changing; but it lives by virtue of its surroundings. Only the surroundings give true value to
the subject.[2]

That was the moment of clarity, the *anagnorisis,* that gave
me a deeper sense of meaning to the reflections you will find
in this book. Janene, dementia, and certainly I, are not the
subjects of the thoughts you are about to read, any more than
a haystack was the subject of Monet's renderings. Winter,
summer, fall, spring, dawn's light, sunset shades, snow, overcast
skies, long and noonday shadows, cloudless skies—they are
all the environmental changes between the "motif and me"
that Monet captures in his series, not unlike the onslaughts
of grief, crushing powerlessness, surprising joy, or a survivor's

guilt we experience in the face of our own particular form of suffering.

Unlike Monet, I didn't aspire to be a writer, an artist. I began journaling simply to make some sense out of my unpredictable and unprecedented responses to the subject matter—my wife's initial uncharacteristic behavior, early dementia diagnosis, ongoing decline, and eventual placement in a memory care facility.

But in its basic architecture, that story, the one about how Janene declined and the unrelenting advances of her rare form of dementia, is remarkably similar to every other caretaker's story. It's the painfully particular description of watching a loved one succumb to a progressive neurological disease for which there is no treatment or cure. Quite frankly, that part of the story, especially with repeated telling, which is so often required, though dramatically painful, turns out to be as boring as a haystack. Like Monet's unique ability to capture the variance in light and seasons, the thing worth observing is the innumerable nuances of our responses to Plan B. The challenge to note is when the life we are now living—due to fate, accident, providence, our bad choices, intentional malevolence, and host of mind-bending reasons—was not our plan.

What you will find in the following pages are reflections on what one of my "book mentors," Parker Palmer, the Quaker educator and author, calls the "tragic gap between our aspirations and dreams and the current reality many of us are living."[3] For me, that was the ever-widening gap between the life Janene and I had spent, hour upon hopeful hour, discussing how we would live in the last quarter of our lives together and witnessing her losing the battle with dementia. Tragic sounds dramatic. But tragic is the only fitting word to describe the extreme distress and sorrow of her decline.

I'm actually not given to parapsychological, spiritual, extrasensory, or second-floor art museum experiences of this mystifying sort. I could count the ones I've had on one hand. I like to put my left brain to good use determining effectiveness. On the other hand, I find the precious few mystical experiences I've had hard to totally discount because they follow this predictable pattern—short, dense, mysterious yet understandable, attached to current reality. They help discern the true meaning of my predicament and connect me to the spiritual world. So when they occur I listen.

So why *am* I writing? Since my "Monet Moment" as I have come to call it, I am offering my experience and thoughts to you in the hopes they will help you navigate your own tragic gap. In the old language of the guild, I'd like to be an apprentice, or maybe even a journeyman of the intangible, in that craft of the spiritual and self-observation required to find meaning in the face of suffering.

My "haystack" is dementia. It's a particular and unique form of Plan B, life derailment, and suffering. Yours may be similar or remarkably different, not easier or harder, just different, and yours alone. But that deep and heartbroken space in our souls that hardship exposes is what we all have in common. There we discover anew our best selves and often are introduced to an unwelcome side of our worst selves. It is that space as Monet describes "between the motif and me"—our internal and spiritual posture toward the immovable haystack in our lives—that I invite you to explore with me on the pages that follow.

One "advantage" of the long goodbye for the Alzheimer's and dementia caregiver that I don't enjoy is the time it offers for reflection and a more contemplative lifestyle. I've learned to adjust to it, though. It's been well over a decade of observing my emotional, social, and spiritual change of seasons on this journey with Janene.

On good days, I am certain to reach the master level in this craft of redemptive suffering. And on bad days, well, I'm an apprentice all over again. But my hope is that these reflections on this prolonged tutorial in which I find myself will offer you a measure of guidance and comfort for the unique terrain of your own journey.

2 | MY ANNIVERSARY

TODAY IS MY 50ᵀᴴ wedding anniversary. *My* anniversary? What an absurdly awkward description. Yet, there's no other way to describe the day. It no longer is *our* anniversary. She had no idea why I greeted her with a dozen red roses today for lunch.

This day, more than any other in the past 15 years of Janene's battle against early onset dementia confirms that I no longer have a soul mate, life companion, lover, confidante, and best friend with whom I can celebrate the tipping points and benchmarks of life. The unyielding march of the disease has long since made celebration, intimacy, connection, relationship, conversation and all that contributes to a good marriage impossible. Frontotemporal Dementia (FTD) has gutted Janene's astonishing capacity to celebrate an event with those she loves.

So I celebrated our 50 years together as best I could with a heart that was grateful, joyful, and deeply broken. My mind wandered back over the decades and relived the traditions Janene and I built into our anniversaries. Food played a big role in our life together as we discovered our favorite anniversary dinner spots like the Flagstaff House in Boulder, The Fort in Golden, Pine Creek Cookhouse near Aspen, Soupcon in Crested Butte, and Steamboat's finest Pan-Asian restaurant with our finest table situated right on the Yampa River. Our day always included the spectacular Rocky Mountain outdoors in which we had spent countless hours together. Downhill and cross-country skiing, snow shoeing, or hiking consistently invigorated our souls and bodies before the celebratory meal together in the evening.

One of our fondest anniversary days ended at the Pine Creek Cookhouse nestled in the mountains just south of Aspen. In the winter, as is our anniversary, the road to the restaurant is closed and the modes of travel over the two-plus miles from the parking area are horse-drawn sleigh, snowshoes, or cross-country skis. Janene and I chose our cross-country skis. After our elk medallions and sea bass, I shall never forget the moonlit trek back down the mountain, stunningly beautiful through fresh powder, and breathtakingly romantic. It was one of those enchanted evenings which I trust you too have experienced, where every detail is forever etched in our memories.

And then, not but 18 months later, Janene and I found ourselves having lunch at the Cookhouse again with family and friends. While reveling in the mountain view and amazing food a second time, I leaned over and whispered into Janene's ear, "Isn't it great to be at the Cookhouse again?"

She had a puzzled look on her face, and her response I shall never forget as well, "I've never been here before, honey."

Dementia will destroy even the dearest and fondest memories… if you let it, if you give it that power.

Suffering, in its innumerable forms, relentlessly attempts to overpower us emotionally and rob us of the truest forms of our humanity. Awash with discouragement, depression, and even despair, we can easily overidentify with these feelings and our internal state and let them define us. Especially when suffering evolves into a chronic life situation, we are susceptible to what psychology calls "learned helplessness"—the sense of powerlessness arising from a traumatic event or continual obstacles. In common parlance we simply say and know folks who "have given up on life."

My response to the shocking onset of Janene's illness was to make a powerless vow that afternoon there in the shadows of Maroon Bells: *I'm never coming back to the Pine Creek Cookhouse again.*

Now, of course, where one decides to experience fine dining is only a first world problem, as we say, and is not life changing. But it illustrates a much larger point. I love everything about the Cookhouse. Ambiance. Views. Menu. Why would I let FTD rob me of the choice to experience both the joy and sadness occasioned in those environs? Isn't the capacity to make life-giving choices in the midst of suffering part of what it means to be human?

Well, as fate, or more likely, Providence would have it, some of my dearest friends from Texas invited me to their small family wedding here in Colorado and where do you suppose they decided to exchange their vows? The Pine Creek Cookhouse. Of course, I accepted this invitation to revisit the locale of enchantment, memory, suffering, and now the occasion of newfound love and life together. It was a dramatically healing and redemptive day for me.

So now the Pine Creek Cookhouse is a symbol of this mysterious convergence that is found in prolonged suffering where pain, grief, loss, gratitude, joy, resilience, blessing, and especially choice, all come together.

Nowhere is this matter of choice in the midst of suffering made more dramatically apparent than in Victor Frankl's life in the concentration camp. Here are Frankl's deep observations in *Man's Search for Meaning* for you to apply to your unique set of circumstances.

> The way in which a man accepts his fate and all the suffering it entails, the way in which he takes up his cross, gives him ample opportunity—even in the most difficult circumstances—to add a deeper meaning to his life.
>
> Does man have no choice of action in the face of such circumstance?
>
> Is there no spiritual freedom in regard to behavior and action to any given surroundings?

...everything can be taken away from a man but one thing: the last of the human freedoms—to choose one's attitude in any given set of circumstances, to choose one's own way.[1]

There is a community of sufferers we join in the face of our own particular challenge. From Frankl to family members, spiritual directors, and honest friends—they all become our guides and mentors along the way. Jerry Sittser, who lost his wife, daughter, and mother in one tragic car accident, describes how his soul grew in *A Grace Disguised*, is one of those guides for me.

Sooner or later all people will suffer loss, in little doses or big ones, suddenly or over time, privately or in public settings. Loss is as much a part of normal life as birth, for as surely as we are born into this world, we suffer loss before we leave it.

It is not, therefore, the experience of loss that becomes the defining moment of our lives, for that is as inevitable as death, which is the last loss awaiting us all. It is how we respond to loss that matters. That response will largely determine the quality, the direction, and the impact of our lives.[2]

So on this my/our 50th anniversary day, I'm going to be heartbroken *and* celebrate. I've had three gut-wrenching cries today... so far. And this evening, I'm going to enjoy the camaraderie and companionship of a dear friend over a good glass of wine. Dementia will not steal my capacity to choose joy and fellowship or celebration. Not even tonight.

I didn't want "the impact of my life" to involve a response to adversity. And none of the good that might somehow or someday come of the suffering Janene and I have endured erases the horror and tragedy of it all. But you and I can choose to live into the tragic gap of our lives with grace and capacious hearts. At least on good days we can. And that choice will make a difference.

3 | GRIM REALITY

JANENE AND I HAD FACED some significant challenges over the course of our 41 years together, but none larger than the one in February of 2011—five days of assessment at the University of California at the San Francisco Memory and Aging Center under the direction of Dr. Bruce Miller. We prepared as best we could for a week of diagnostic work in the face of Janene's subtle but steady cognitive decline.

Degenerative neurological disorders have neither a cure nor a treatment. I had done enough research to know what we were facing and what the outcome of Janene's evaluation was likely to be. Still, I felt confident Janene and I were going to be in good hands for the week of painful evaluation.

Early in the testing process, I met alone with a clinical RN. I faced the harsh truth as she asked me a series of questions.

"When did you first notice the change in Janene?"

"What changes have you seen in her personality in the past few years?"

"Is she less affectionate and a bit more self-centered than she used to be?"

"Do you notice more rigidity and the need for more structure in her life?"

"Is she as aware of the process and dynamics of a conversation as before?"

I shared my observations of the emotional and mental changes in Janene, the social miscues like asking for a friend's leftovers from a nice dinner or going to bed unannounced when friends were over for dinner, along with incidents of her memory loss and confusion.

The nurse's face was kind and her eyes were filled with some sort of seasoned compassion. She knew and she knew that I knew.

"This must be very difficult for you, Jay."

I cried. She reached for the Kleenex. There were no words between us.

At the end of the week, after many more questions and much testing, Janene and I sat down with Dr. Miller to receive Janene's formal diagnosis. It was at this point we learned the technical name of Janene's nemesis. Janene is battling Frontotemporal Dementia.

Frontotemporal Dementia (FTD) is devastating to its victims and their loved ones. FTD gradually robs people of basic abilities—thinking, talking, walking, socializing—that we all take for granted. It often strikes people in the prime of life, when they are working and raising families.

FTD frequently begins with nerve cell loss in the frontal lobe of the brain (behind the forehead), affecting self-awareness, social decorum, language ability, decision making, and setting priorities of daily life. Common symptoms include apathy, depression, and lack of drive. And then there are the changes in emotional behaviors—exaggerated responses, flatness, or feelings expressed at the wrong time like laughing at sad news. In common parlance we simply say their personality is changing.

The temporal lobe, located below the frontal lobe and behind the ears, helps us understand words, speak, write, and connect words with meanings. It helps people recognize objects, including faces, and relate the appropriate emotions to events and objects. It can be said that the frontal lobe manages emotional and social intelligence, and the temporal lobe manages language and cognitive tasks. When both are declining, the impact on the individual and her family are enormous.

Janene's specific diagnosis with the FTD disorder, Dr. Miller informed us, is *progressive primary aphasia*. This includes decline in the ability to communicate, to use language accurately and appropriately, speak, write, understand others, reason, memory, and judgment.

Few physical ailments confront the scientific mind and pastoral heart regarding the definition of personhood and the meaning of persons like dementia and Alzheimer's disease. We are faced with a disease for which there is no identifiable cause and for which there is no cure, especially early onset dementia.

Advanced MRIs and PET scans now offer extraordinary descriptions of the results of the disease, but not the cause of these neurological disorders. As a leading ALZ researcher responded in a Charlie Rose interview some years ago when pressed for why the medical community isn't making more progress, "We are at least a decade away from understanding why the brain cells are dying, so we can't develop a pharmacological solution."[1]

I will not soon forget the surprised look on the face of Dr. Bruce Miller when he discovered that absolutely no one on either side of Janene's family had ever been touched by a degenerative neurological disorder. This renowned neurologist, researcher, and director of the UCSF Center for Memory and Aging, whose staff had conducted five days of intense diagnostic evaluation on Janene, could only shake his head in disbelief. As UCSF is a teaching hospital, with European psychiatrists, Stanford trained PhD neurologists, and a bevy of highly-trained professionals in the room, along with our three daughters, Dr. Miller had the courage to put into words what was etched on everyone's face observing him manage the case feedback session for our family after evaluating Janene's disorder… "We know so little about this disease. Janene, we don't know why you got it and there is no certain treatment."

Generally, those of us schooled in the Western tradition of science and reason are not so good with mystery and the baffling. At least a bit of comfort might be found if there was a genetic predisposition in this ailment that has robbed Janene of her brilliant mind, identity, and personhood. While it wouldn't change a thing, we might be able to quiet our logical, cause and effect, explanation demanding minds, perhaps even a little, if we were certain of why she is so afflicted.

But on this day the only comfort to be found was in the intensely compassionate face of Dr. Miller as he delivered to Janene and our family the grim reality of our altered future.

4 | FORGIVENESS

THE INTAKE INTERVIEW at the Memory and Aging Center was led by a young Stanford graduate student in neurology. Our meeting with her had progressed as one might expect with all the normal questions about age, children, location, home ownership, occupation, marital status and such. The student did a thorough job explaining the scope of the center's assessment protocols with numerous MRIs, PET scans, and extensive interviews which, as you can imagine, left Janene trying her best to understand and left me attempting to absorb what I intuitively knew was about to change my life.

My elevated anxiety had begun to subside as we finished the intake, when our heretofore kind and gentle interviewer reached into her folder and rigidly shoved a document across the desk. She looked at me and shocked my system with these unforgettable words: "Here, we need you to sign this Autopsy

Consent Form for our research study."

I was instantly adrenalized and shocked. Janene was completely confused. I gathered myself after what seemed like an interminable silence to respond with, "No, I'm not prepared to sign an autopsy consent."

We left the intake interview, and I put the audacious thought of an autopsy out of my mind for the rest of the week.

Somewhere over the Utah salt flats, while Janene was asleep beside me on our return flight home, I found myself debriefing the grueling five-day San Francisco experience. I walked myself through the process from the intake interview to the final case review with Dr. Miller. Then this burning sensation arose in my chest. My throat wasn't able to navigate my soft drink. I had, of course, recalled the moment of the Autopsy Consent Form.

What I have come to realize over the last decade is that this young UCSF intake interviewer introduced me to a surprising reality of any journey of suffering—it requires an undaunted spirit of forgiveness. In a strange sort of way, I'm grateful to her. She was simply following the protocol. Her intentions were clearly not to cause additional pain for us, though she certainly did. But she played a certain midwifery role for me in that she assisted in the development and brought into being a necessary approach for suffering well, or at least handling it better than I might have otherwise.

It is one thing to admit to myself I've been hurt, whether the offense is actually a trivial matter or a life-changing catastrophic mistake on the part of the offender. Forgiveness is quite another.

On our return trip from SF, I was in no way ready to let it go. I was holding on to my moral superiority, judgment, and astonishment at the lack of emotional intelligence. We aren't required to forgive. It's a choice. But, as author Anne Lamott puts it so bluntly, "Not forgiving is like drinking rat poison and waiting for the rats to die."[1]

As we know so well, when drinking rat poison any of us can become resentful, bitter, jaded, grudge holding, cynical, mean, cruel, caustic, harsh, strident, cutting, corrosive, unfriendly, scathing, indignant, incensed, hostile, distant, detached, aloof. The list goes on and on in blatant or camouflaged forms when we withhold forgiveness.

I've had a good bit of practice in the last decade of Janene's illness trying as best I could to forgive, to extend grace. For instance, not but three days after the county sheriff deputy took Janene to the local hospital emergency room, the case manager called to announce they were discharging her, though neither they nor I could find a memory care facility that would accept her uncommon condition. A few months later a neuropsychiatrist treated us with dramatic disregard and lack of professionalism. Three memory-care facilities assured me they were equipped to handle the early stages of Janene's aggressive exit seeking, yet within weeks announced, "You will need to find another placement for your wife." During one particularly difficult week, the memory-care staff and I followed the local hospital's protocol to have an ALZ or dementia patient admitted to their geriatric/psych unit for evaluation only to have the emergency room physician refuse admission because she "failed to show a psychiatric history."

I discovered, like many of you have, that I must find a way to forgive systems like our medical system when it fails to deliver on behalf of those we love so dearly, and we find all our best advocacy efforts somehow falling short in the face of institution structures. It's painful to watch a loved one suffer unnecessarily at the hands of organizations that claim to be there to serve us well in times of pain or crisis. There are, it seems to me, "powers that be" which somehow become embedded in institutions where otherwise well-trained and well-intentioned professionals at times appear to be serving the dark side rather than the well-being of those we love. I am still trying to forgive these impersonal and institutional forms of disappointment. It's a challenge.

And on a more personal level, if your faith, community, family, neighbors, or circle of close friends have consistently met your need for support and connection, consider yourself among the precious few. Most experience an unsettling gap here. Some of the folks in our pre-suffering life who we would have sworn would go the distance with us, we came to discover actually cannot do so. And then too, the most unlikely others will rise to the occasion and fearlessly walk the road with us. The former need to be accepted, forgiven, and the latter enjoyed.

And when a dear friend or colleague assures me that "this is God's plan and we just don't understand it," I strive to be forgiving since I too have offered up a trite advisory word in the face of the insolvable when attempting to manage my own wordlessness and angst.

Then too, in a well-intended effort to ease my emotional pain in the face of dementia's unrelenting encroachment on my wife Janene's quality of life, both friends and a few professionals have offered false reassurances. These partial truths come in a variety of forms. Some of the most commons ones over the past decade have been:

"You know Janene really isn't here anymore."

Or, "She has forgotten so much of your history and life together."

Or again, "People with FTD (Frontotemporal Dementia) can't do cause and effect thinking anymore."

And even banal exhortations such as… "Just take care of yourself since Janene doesn't really remember if you have visited her or not."

When current reality is inexplicably and absurdly mysterious, it is no surprise that we grasp for comforting straws. It is for good reason folks offer up platitudes and partial truths to a good friend in the face of yet another expression of the impenetrable mysteries of life. I wonder how often I have done the same.

It is no small task to humbly bow before the unknowable and life-altering mystery. Few have the spiritual or psychological maturity, or maybe the character to do so gracefully. Part of the challenge for me is to offer grace and forbearance to those, who out of the goodness of their hearts, are attempting to lighten the grief and loss that must certainly be evident in my eyes and voice. However misguided it may be, they are, I know, just trying to lend a helping hand and are doing the best they can.

Along with institutions and people, I have had a few arguments with God as well. My complaints have been along the lines of the old gospel song, "Farther Along," which goes like this...

Tempted and tried we're oft made to wonder
Why it should be thus all the daylong
While there are others living about us
Never molested though in the wrong

When death has come and taken our loved ones
It leaves our home so lonely and drear
And then do we wonder why others prosper
Living so wicked year after year[2]

Quite frankly, I've had to forgive God for not holding up His end of the faulty bargain I made with the Prosperity Gospel—one we all believe to greater or lesser degrees that health, wealth, and happiness is our birthright if we do our best—and then discover how angry and scandalized we are when suddenly we're on Plan B as expressed in these lyrics. In its simplest form the Prosperity Gospel is the belief originating in some streams of Judeo-Christian thought, that if I am a good person, I will live a privileged life. That if I follow the Golden Rule, then I will be assured of blessings—especially financial blessing. It's an emotional bargain made with God, or the Universe, or our Higher Power. And often we are clueless that the bargain was struck until things go awry. Then a trap door of emotions comes unhinged. Religious doubts, philosophic questions, and often the shadow side of ourselves we hardly knew existed comes out of hiding. Someone or something must be to blame. Usually God. Maybe even life itself.

I hate to admit to some thread of spiritual bypassing in the back closet of my worldview, hoped that if I try hard, adhere to a moral compass, and love my quirky neighbors most of the time, then I will get a pass on suffering. That one stuck to me like the proverbial bark on a tree. How preposterous, letting God off the hook for a deal He didn't make in the first place.

Actually, it seems to me that God's "deal" with us is that *nothing* will separate us from His love. Pure and simple. And that is exactly what I experience if I am willing to forgive. Maybe it's Life itself that must be forgiven for not working out the way we had all hoped.

When it has become apparent over the course of this passage with Janene that yet another round of forgiveness is required, I have puzzled over a disturbingly relevant response of Jesus on this topic. One of his devotees asked him, "How often should I forgive my brother? Seven?" Jesus' unexpected reply is, "Not seven, but seventy times seven."[3]

Personally, I like the rabbinical tradition of Jesus' day that recommended three times, especially if I'm inclined to nurse a grudge. But seeing forgiveness as a process with no limits, a way of life, a boundless source of grace and mercy to the offender, that's a large challenge, especially when I'm in this interminable period of loss and grief. And, on the other hand, I love the freedom that comes with letting it go, ending the silent treatment, or getting off my moral high horse. I suspect both Anne Lamott and Jesus were right about this matter of forgiveness.

So I forgave the young grad student for her naïve insensitivity. I also agreed to sign the autopsy consent form, though it was several years after the San Francisco visit. Knowing Janene's passion for medical science and education, and her dedication to the ways of Jesus, I believe that's what she would want.

When I have exhausted my mediocre capacity to forgive, when the need to let go of the trivial or monumental hurt is evident once again, I turn to this prayer, scratched by an unknown hand on the inner walls of a concentration camp in Nazi Germany. May it be an inspiration for you as it so often has been for me.

O Lord, when I shall come with glory into your kingdom, do not remember only the men of good will; remember also the men of evil. May they be remembered not only for their acts of cruelty in this camp, the evil they have done to us prisoners, but balance against their cruelty the fruits we have reaped under the stress and in the pain; the comradeship, the courage, the greatness of heart, the humility and patience which have been born in us and become part of our lives, because we have suffered at their hands. May the memory of us not be a nightmare to them when they stand in judgment? May all that we have suffered be acceptable to you as a ransom for them.[4]

5 | LONELINESS AND SOLITUDE

IT'S NEARLY UNBELIEVABLE that a person could navigate decades of life and never truly taste loneliness. But that's my experience. I was the third-born with two older brothers who loved me. It is not an exaggeration to say I had adoring aunts, uncles, and grandparents, with a plethora of cousins on Mom's side of the family. All embedded in the religious, agrarian, interdependent 1960s human architecture of a Mennonite subculture in southeastern Iowa. Loneliness was both a foreign concept and unknown experience.

During my high school years, we farm boys roamed around the community looking for good and ill to do much like a wolf pack. Fishing for bullheads on Deer Creek with Bob Yoder 'til 2:00 in the morning or "raiding" a high school girl's slumber party with my tribe, I was never alone. I grew up in an activity-rich and relationship-rich environment. Opportunity for adventure abounded and a whole cadre of boys awaited the chance to join in.

Marriage and family simply built on this foundation of extroverted, community-based experience. To have a smart, verbal, relationship-oriented wife was a dream come true. I had a conversation partner 24-7. Then add to the mix three attractive, engaging, intelligent, and high-energy daughters. Plus, our middle daughter was the social coordinator for her large and energetic peer group all through middle school and high school. Our home on Costilla Avenue was activity central for well over a decade.

By the time our youngest was off to the University of Colorado, Janene and I had built a solid network of friends and professional colleagues. Yes, we had a few empty nest adjustments to make, but ours was a relationship-rich life fully engaged in a faith community and professional efforts. I was not alone, and amazingly, knew almost nothing of the anguish common to loneliness and the challenge it is to emotional and spiritual well-being.

This sheltered reality abruptly changed that October morning in 2015 when I turned my back on the scene, forever riveted in my mind's eye, of Deputy Lebsack driving away with Janene as his passenger. I walked back through the garage, laundry room, and then into the vacuous silence of what was now my kitchen, not ours.

But truth be told, the loneliness began a decade prior. One word, one social miscue, one request for a spelling after another, one more puzzled look, one forgotten friend, another forgotten moment we once shared, one unlike Janene behavior after another—as her essential self slipped away from her and from me, she left me increasingly alone for well over a decade before the morning her body left our home.

Rachel Hadas describes this October loneliness of mine in her memoir of her husband George's dementia as "a sharply etched loneliness—a loneliness that stepped out of the shadows to which I had so far consigned it right onto center stage."[1] Yes indeed, the curtains to a life of essential aloneness were pulled back, and I was now a center stage actor in a drama I would have given nearly anything to avoid.

It is sometimes said of Alzheimer's and dementia that it is a death that leaves the body behind. Painfully true and descriptive. The long goodbye is another of Alzheimer's graphic descriptions that attempts to capture the agonizingly slow loss of the loved one from the degenerative neurological disease. Perhaps the worst sort of loneliness is that of dementia, or Alzheimer's. The body is there but the soul is gone. Companionship is no longer possible. Some of you know firsthand this heart-sickening loneliness.

It seems that over a lifetime, by whatever means it finds our whereabouts, there are precious few who escape the relentless pursuit of loneliness. Along with you, I have received the dreaded phone call when the other voice informed us that a mother, a professional partner, a spouse, and even a child was gone—mind, soul, and body. Gone. All of the person is forever no longer here. The call announces that life as we knew it had changed instantly, and that we are, in all probability, thrust into a fathomless season of loneliness.

Whether loneliness comes in the life-altering call or seeps gradually into our lives as it did for me, it will arrive. It's just a matter of time. There is some comfort to be found in the thoughts of Jean Vanier in his bestseller, *Becoming Human*. He believes that "loneliness is something essential to human nature; it can only be covered over, it can never actually go away."[2] And he writes that the darkest seasons of our lives are often the source of creativity, new energy and direction for what could lie ahead. Were it not for my reluctant introduction to loneliness and my exposure to its grasp, you would not be reading these reflections.

Not only is loneliness the seedbed for creative energy, Vanier claims that loneliness is the fundamental force that urges humanity toward a deeper union with God. Instead of slipping into forms of apathy, despair, self-pity, or bitterness, it is this keen sense of isolation that creates the possibility of movement toward the Transcendent.

That may be what happened to me in these last few years without Janene. Because to my utter amazement, about two years into Janene's departure, I found myself finally dry-eyed when going to the grocery store. Planting a garden for the second season was almost as joyful as when Janene planned and planted our beloved plot. And this place where I now live, the two-plus acres that Janene and I were so dramatically blessed to have purchased and built our modest dream home on, has actually become a sanctuary for me. I love the lawn care, snow removal, tree trimming, and even the home repair. My single occupancy of the home and property that Janene and I filled with so much love and companionship for 30 years has become a "sacred place of refuge and safety," a retreat from the unyielding advance of dementia. A sanctuary. How could this be possible? It seems I am making the transition from loneliness to solitude.

My perspective and experience were informed by one of the most influential thinkers regarding matters of the soul in the 20th century. Paul Tillich, German American theologian, academic, and Harvard Divinity School professor, weighs in on this experience of companionlessness that finally caught up with me and awaits us all. In *The Eternal Now*, Tillich makes explicit what we all know to be true and yet resist when it enters the reality of our day-to-day lives.

> Being alive means being in a body—a body separated from all other bodies. And being separated means being alone. This is true of every creature, and it is more true of man than any other creature. He is not only alone; he knows that he is alone. Aware of what he is, he asks questions of his loneliness. Neither can he escape it. It is his destiny to be alone and to be aware of it. Not even God can take this destiny away from him.[3]

I am reminded of one of the sweetest seasons of my life with Janene, shortly after the youngest of our three daughters had left for college. We were in the flow spiritually, emotionally, sexually, professionally, physically… life was good. That was the year Janene took me to a special spot on top of Rabbit Ears Pass with a stunning view of the Yampa Valley to open my anniversary present—the finely wrapped cover only of a fancy Weber BBQ grill she bought and I always wanted but for which I was unwilling to spend the money. She read my mind. We were in a period of deep and rich intimacy and communion.

And as was our custom at that time, we were celebrating our anniversary in Steamboat Springs along the flowing Yampa River at our favorite Pan-Asian eatery and our favorite table after a day of snowshoeing in the Rockies. It was then that Janene reached across the table, took my hand, and as her enormous, pristine, blue eyes brimmed with tears spoke directly into the reality of which Tillich writes. "I love you with all my heart. We are so close and yet so far away."

While there were precious few things that Tillich and Elvis might have had in common, remember the lyrics of a rarely unpopular song by Elvis?

> *So close, yet so far from paradise*
> *I hold, you in my arms, in paradise*
> *Is mine, then you slip away*
> *Like a child at play, and here am I*
> *So close, yet so far from paradise*[4]

Tillich, with his brilliant insight speaks further into this conundrum, this paradox of life in which we all have or will find ourselves when confronted with the departure, separation, or death of those who have helped us forget that we are alone.

> Our language has wisely sensed these two sides of man's being alone. It has created the word "loneliness" to express the pain of being alone. And it created the word "solitude" to express the glory of being alone.
>
> Loneliness can only be conquered by those who can bear solitude. We have a natural desire for solitude…We want to feel what we are—namely, alone—not in pain and sorrow, but with joy and courage. There are many ways in which solitude can be sought and experienced. And each way can be called "religious," if it is true, as one philosopher said, that "religion is what man does with solitariness."[5]

Perhaps this is why we can spend hours in the silence of nature. There is some unspoken language of the forest, or ocean, or the mountains that helps us move from loneliness to solitude. For you it might be music, poetry, art, or extended periods of intentional quiet and contemplation. But whatever your preferred path to solitude, seek it, use it well, for it is clear we are the better for having faced the loneliness head on with courage.

Tillich ends his reflection with an appeal of the risk and satisfaction of finding the transcendent in the midst of our solitude with these lofty and challenging thoughts.

> In these moments of solitude something is done to us. The center of our being, the innermost self that is the ground of our aloneness, is elevated to the divine center and taken into it. Therein can we rest without losing ourselves. In the poverty of solitude all riches are present. Let us dare to have solitude—to face the eternal, to find others, and see ourselves.[6]

And finally, may I leave you with the challenge I have found helpful from the last lines of "The Invitation," a poem by Oriah Mountain Dreamer.

> *It doesn't interest me where or what or with whom you have studied. I want to know what sustains you from the inside when all else falls away.*
> *I want to know if you can be alone with yourself and if you truly like the company you keep in the empty moments.*[7]

6 | "MY HEART BREAKS WITH YOURS"

HE WAS SITTING in a wheelchair, all 6'5" of his robust frame, stuffed awkwardly into this untimely mode of transportation. A freakish accident on his road bike and this rarest of hip fractures required his 10-week confinement. However restricted his body may have been, his mind and soul were vibrant and fully functional as we enjoyed reconnecting after many months.

We were together for business and strategic planning for our respective non-profit ventures. Both of us are avid cyclists and so his detailed account of the accident, the lack of memory as to the cause, the angst that it may be a neurological event all seemed necessary to our reconnecting before we got down to the work at hand. He joked that I was "the lucky dog" for recently completing my third Ride the Rockies 450-mile biking tour across Colorado.

Then it just poured from my soul—the pain, loss, frustration, loneliness, fear, and distress with Janene's FTD. I recounted how Janene made deep connections to our home and virtually everything and everyone in her life. Her love for our three daughters and me was without reserve. She nurtured high school friendships that began decades ago. Back in the early days of our family, her love for health and wellness offered up nutburgers for dinner, much to the chagrin of our girls. Then in recent years this passion for wellness led Janene to write a book and start a company for mid-life women's health. Her love for nature and the outdoors took the form of hiking, camping, backpacking, skiing, snowshoeing, climbing Colorado's 14ers, and most of all, road biking, logging upwards of 75-plus miles a week until the day she entered memory care. Twice she jumped out of an airplane skydiving to express her love of adventure. She loved food. When her dementia made any form of employment impossible, she began Janene's Gourmet Cooking to serve homebound folks in our church and neighborhood. Her connection to the spiritual realm and God was deep and abiding. My wife had this rare and extraordinary capacity to be fully present to the whole of life—spiritual, interpersonal, natural, and emotional. There was nothing detached and aloof about this woman. And now she was gradually fading away from all of it, me included.

He listened as I bore my anguish.

At long last, after I had detailed the precarious emotional and diagnostic journey of the past few years and framed the daunting task of being a faith-based existentialist, my friend, confidante, and fellow sojourner leaned back in his wheelchair, and with tears in his eyes and pain in his face, simply uttered these words:

"My heart breaks with yours."

There were no false reassurances, no fundamentalist triumphalism, no trite biblical admonitions, no anxious platitudes, not even some appropriate connection with his own physical dilemma. None of that.

Empathy—the capacity to understand and feel what another person is experiencing from within their frame of reference—is, of course, what my friend offered to me. The common and oft-used phrase that attempts to capture this remarkable ability to place oneself in another's experience is "walk a mile in their shoes." He is amongst a host of family members, friends, colleagues, neighbors, and clients who have given voice to their remarkable capacity to empathize with me as I have watched Janene concede to the unabated advance of dementia. I am grateful for each of them.

But "my heart breaks with yours" is no insignificant line. It speaks to a bond we all share as human beings. It gives voice to our human potential to connect with each other deeply and emotionally. It's the material of soulmates. It goes well beyond "I'm so sorry" or "You'll be in my thoughts and prayers." My friend's response unmistakably said to me, "right here, right now, at this moment in time and space, our souls are united in this plight of yours." And it embraces *together* the archetypal reality of our human condition and a word we hesitate to use—suffering.

Now it turns out the friend I'm referencing here is the Right Reverend Episcopal Bishop of Colorado, Rob O'Neill.[1] If ever there was an opportune time for a brilliant, episcopal, spiritual platitude, which, by the way, we Anglicans are often skilled at delivering, this was it. But no, instead I instantly knew here was a traveling companion for the complicated and turbulent journey ahead with Janene.

I am reminded of a question posed by another "man of the cloth" (that 17th century way of referring to clergy), William McNamara, the Carmelite and author of *The Human Adventure*. He wonders with all of our refined spirituality, oriental wisdom, mind-expanding drugs, superior psychological and pedagogic methods, plethora of religious literature, retreats, workshops and programs—"Why is it that we, with all this machinery at our disposal and such a mass of goodwill, are not all saints? I venture to say it is because we are not human enough. We dare not let ourselves become human beings."[2]

So may I pass along to you the wisdom and insight of these spiritual leaders and simply encourage us all to let our hearts break with each other in the face of adversity and distress.

7 | ZUCCHINI MUFFINS

I ALWAYS BELIEVED in the old adage that "laughter is the best medicine," until it became painfully obvious that Janene was losing that brilliant mind of hers. Then I became, at least a good bit of the time, a sourpuss, that slang phrase my dad used to attach to one or all of us three boys when things didn't go our way as young farm boys. As you know, that term is reserved for the person who is habitually sullen, grouchy, bad-tempered, and pouty. Of course, there were more than a few reasons to be in a gloomy mood when facing the prospect of life with a Frontotemporal Dementia afflicted partner. FTD, like any form of hardship, will relentlessly siphon the joy out of life and wipe the smile off your face; that is, if you let it or give it the power to do so.

Unbeknownst to me before FTD, this matter of tragedy and humor has been a topic of serious thought and even scholarship. Victor Frankl, our exemplar of surviving the unthinkable Auschwitz and Dachau, made the startling comment that even in the concentration camp, "Humor was another of the soul's weapons in the fight for self-preservation. It is well known that humor, more than anything else in the human makeup, can afford an aloofness and an ability to rise above any situation, even if only for a few seconds."[1]

Or again from those darkest of times when a day's meal was a piece of stale bread and a cup of rotting soup, Elie Wiesel in his memoir of the concentration camp reports hearing one prisoner say to another, "Hey Moshe, don't overeat. Think of us who will have to carry you."[2]

It seems that humor has helped us see our situation, no matter how dire it is or seems to us, with a bit of objectivity, even if for a fleeting moment.

And who would have guessed that religion and humor would have something in common—seeing familiar things in new ways. Isn't it true that all religions, East and West alike, encourage us to look at the challenges of our lives from a different angle? Take for instance the Zen Buddhist quip: "My barn burned down and now I have a better view of the rising moon."

Even the scientific community has put its scholarship to work on how humor affects our biochemistry. The claim is that humor enhances our brain chemistry and releases dopamine, that powerful neurotransmitter that promotes our sense of well-being and pleasure.

Well, this is all to say that even I have had occasion to smile and sometimes laugh out loud along this otherwise arduous terrain with FTD. And without any publishable study in a journal of neurology, I can tell laughter aligns my biochemistry for the better. Here's an example:

By August of 2015 our zucchini plants were supplying squash to all the neighbors and beyond, as is their custom. The zucchini surplus coincided with Janene's unrelenting drive to reclaim her driver's license months after her doctor, the Department of Motor Vehicles, and I had suspended her privileges to do so. On several occasions she had ridden her road bike, now her only means of transportation, the five miles to the DMV and taken the driver's exam only to have failed it repeatedly. This was, by the way, the first time in her life that Janene had anything less than an A on a test of any sort—high school, college, and graduate school alike.

So on this particular summer morning, Janene baked a boatload of zucchini muffins, loaded them in her backpack, jumped on her road bike, destined for the local DMV. It was reported to me later that she entered the DMV office in a chipper mood and promptly handed a still warm muffin to each of the employees and then set about to take the exam yet another time. Seated next to others at their computer screens Janene commenced to ask those to her right and left in her louder than average voice, what an intersection might be, if they knew what a four-way stop sign is, or if they had ever heard of parallel parking.

This did not set well with the manager of the office, of course, and she told Janene that was cheating and therefore not allowed. Janene reassured her that was not the case and that she was only asking good questions of her friends. As she was being ushered out the door, Janene made a comment characteristic of FTD sufferers who can no longer determine and express degrees of emotional stress or discomfort they are experiencing. "I'm going to kill myself if I can't get a driver's license."

The Arapahoe County Sheriff was alerted, who in turn called me while I was within 20 minutes of boarding my flight at Denver International Airport for a business trip to Louisiana. As many of you know, a call of that sort from the police adrenalizes the system as few things can. He apprised me of the situation and said he would call when contact was made with Janene.

Nine minutes and 30 long seconds later, since I was keeping track, Deputy Lebsack called back with a chuckle and lightness in his voice reassuring me that Janene was just fine as, "Your pretty wife greeted me at the front door and asked if I would like a fresh baked zucchini muffin."

The story is told that in the early years of the turmoil in Ireland an Ulster shopkeeper who had his storefront damaged in a bomb attack remained undaunted. He placed a sign out front with the words "More Open Than Usual" and business continued.

A social critic said it well that, "For a few moments, under the spell of laughter, the whole of man is completely and gloriously alive: body, mind, and soul... the mind flings open its doors and windows... its foul and secret places are ventilated and sweetened."

And finally, I am reminded of George Santayana's paraphrased quote as pertaining to the group of men with whom I now identify, "The old man who can't laugh is a fool."[3]

8 | "YOU ARE NOT RESPONSIBLE"

COULD VERIZON'S coverage extend to the farthest reaches of the Craig wilderness at no less than 9,000 feet elevation? Apparently. Nestled against the side of an aspen tree, awaiting the improbable emergence of a bull elk on this my 15th hunt, I was certain no one could reach me to interrupt my first afternoon. I was wrong.

Shockingly, my phone rang with David, a friend from church, calling to give me an unwelcome physical and psychological shot of adrenaline.

"We are concerned about Janene because Rebecca and Ellen can't reach her on the phone."

Nothing demands more objectivity than remaining a non-anxious person when your spouse keeps wondering if life's worth living and wanting to end it all. It is small comfort that this may well be one of the ways an FTD patient expresses the intensity of frustration when words are no longer there, especially when they had the IQ that Janene once had. It is wishful thinking to suppose one can be prepared for this.

I reassured David and called Janene only to find out she was fine. She could not recall when I was coming home and wondered, in her customary nurturant way, what I wanted for dinner when I arrived Wednesday evening.

It would be catastrophic for me if Janene completed a suicide attempt. Nonetheless, I have, with God's help, tried my best to at least relinquish as gracefully as possible even this unimaginable challenge.

But on this particular day it seemed as though all the preparation and relinquishment were gone in a heartbeat, and I was panic-stricken all over again, imagining the worst. And, I was disturbed that my time away on the family elk hunt would be so rudely interrupted with this painful call.

Then, just as the sun was disappearing behind the jagged peaks of the Rockies on the perfectly clear and wind-still evening, I heard The Voice.

"You are not responsible for how long Janene is here, I am."

This Voice has caught my attention on precious few and surprising occasions over the decades of my spiritual journey, but none more clear or tender than these words. I have never felt more relief, more contentment, and a deeper peace that passed any way of understanding the complexity of this daunting challenge that found me even in the remotest reaches of the Rockies.

After my call with Janene, reporting back to David that she was fine, and with my heartrate returning to normal, the silence of the forest and fading late afternoon light offered an opportunity to ask that age-old question that the best of minds have struggled with for centuries—do we live in a personal universe? At no time is that question more often asked than when random accident, illness, and tragedy strike. Given what I just reported from The Voice and absorbing the stunning grandeur of a Colorado sunset from timberline, I'm not sure the Big Bang Theory of an impersonal expansion over 13.8 billion years from a point of singularity to who we are and what we have now is very satisfying. At least on this particular evening it falls well short of explaining what just happened on the back side of Quake Mountain, 23.1 miles north of Craig, elevation 9,100 feet, in twilight's fading glow. Perhaps it takes less faith to believe there is a Creator.

9 | HOLIDAYS WITHOUT HER

THE UNIMAGINABLE happened. Janene ran away from home after her driver's license had been successfully suspended and I, adding insult to her injury, confiscated her road bike. She was trapped in our home, left to battle the irreversible advance of her dementia. So, she decided to go, and the only alternative left for me was to engage the law. I was in no way prepared for what happened.

On October 29, 2015, Janene was escorted from our home by Arapahoe County Sheriff Deputy Lebsack and delivered to the emergency room of the local hospital. The image of her bending down to position herself in the back of that police car is forever seared in my memory.

Her departure didn't catch me completely off guard. It had been a long time in the making, several years in fact. It is one thing to prepare oneself as best we can for what we know is inevitable, and quite another to then look a life-changing reality in the eye.

Our life together had become truncated and sure; I had thought she might eventually reside in memory care. But I never imagined the police would cart her off. It was an uncivil, pitiless, cruel way to leave your home of 30 years for no fault of your own. The whole scene still ricochets through my body and off the walls of my mind.

I somehow knew she was never coming back.

When I walked back into the house that late October morning, I saw everything from a poignantly new and shock-filled perspective. It's as if my mind took a picture that morning in a desperate attempt to memorialize what would never be the same. There were the breakfast dishes on the kitchen counter; the *Jesus Calling*, her favorite devotional guide basking in the morning sun on our breakfast table; a manila folder full of calls she hoped to make that day; the frozen chicken breast she had set out to include in our salad for lunch; the double oven and granite countertops she thought were extravagant; and our kitchen, scene of the many thousand meals she prepared with her considerable culinary skill and deep expressions of love.

And then, then the tears flowed uncontrollably. These were tears like I had never cried before. They were, as Emily Dickinson describes so graphically, "tears so hot they almost scald my eyeballs."[1]

Sensitive to Thanksgiving just a few short weeks later as my first holiday without Janene, longtime friends of ours,

Steve and Janie, invited me to join them come Thursday. My nephew thoughtfully reached out, welcoming me to their home an hour away. And there were still others who were willing to set *one* additional chair at their table and to watch the Dallas Cowboys play their traditional game. I turned all the invitations down as best I could. It is simply too painful to show up alone even with friends and family on this first holiday without my companion of 40-plus years.

Truth be told, I made a conscious, deliberate choice to be alone over this first solitary holiday. Of course, it would have been socially and emotionally awkward to be the only one without a partner. But that's not really why I declined the gracious invitations. I "wanted" to be alone. I wanted to wrestle with the power of loss and see how I fared. I wanted to see what surrender might yield.

My decision to look grief in the eye was informed by the insights of folks in the midst of their own grief like Elizabeth Gilbert in a TED Interview:

> There is a humility that you have to step into, where you surrender to being moved through the landscape of grief by grief itself. And it has its own timeframe, it has its own itinerary with you, it has its own power over you, and it will come when it comes. It arrives—it's this tremendously forceful arrival and it cannot be resisted without you suffering more…The posture that you take

is you hit your knees in absolute humility. But to stiffen, to resist, and to fight it is to hurt yourself.

There are certain things that happen to you as a human being that you cannot control or command, that will come to you at really inconvenient times, and where you have to bow in human humility...[2]

My form of humble surrender to the power of The Disease and its acute impact on me that first Thanksgiving with Janene in a memory care facility was to spend the long weekend alone at Ghost Ranch in northern New Mexico at the suggestion of a dear friend. This is a 21,000-acre retreat center located near the village of Abiquiú, which at one time was the home and studio of Georgia O'Keefe as well as the subject of many of her paintings.

Though my three daughters were well informed of my decision to spend Thanksgiving alone and wholeheartedly supported me in doing so, it was still intensely awkward to walk into the only hotel in Abiquiú for their buffet dinner, alone. The hostess greeted me with the understandable question, "Just one?" Laughter and joy flowed from all the tables. There were, of course, no other solitary diners. Several glasses of chenin blanc from the local Black Mesa Winery diluted my discomfort just a bit. Then as you might guess, the turkey was dry, the mashed potatoes were lumpy, the dressing nothing to compare with Janene's southern cornbread offering, green beans in the casserole were canned, and I'm sure they bought the pumpkin pie at the local Walmart. That's the way I remember it anyway. But if Janene or my girls had been sitting across the table from me, it might have been a marvelous meal.

I found myself in Coyote Cabin #3 on Mesa Road isolated well above the main ranch lodge in a spartanly equipped room with a steady drizzle outside and the palpable desert darkness. This may well have been a bad idea.

Ghost Ranch is said to have a certain mystique about it, this place that O'Keefe came to love and to hold dear as she so often expressed in her painting. But the real treasure of this ranch and terrain, according to the original owner, Arthur Pack, nearly one hundred years ago, was "in the understanding of God's love and the overwhelming sense of His living presence here."[3] I appreciate Mr. Pack's perspective, his words imprinted on a stone memorial site overlooking Ghost Ranch. But in this desolate place on this dismal rain-soaked night… not so much. I felt neither the love of God nor His presence.

I am among the fortunate few for whom depression and despair are virtually unknowns. A good enough family, strong and content parents, roots in rural Iowa, no early trauma or tragedy, a loving extended family, a healthy body, two good older brothers… both nature and nurture protected me from what is for many an early and often experience of the dark side of life. I was and am still blessed.

But on this night, there in the confines of Ghost Ranch, I was making an acquaintance, perhaps for the first time, with despair. I know it had been knocking at my door for several years with the knowledge that this day of aloneness would eventually come as I watched the essential personhood of my soul mate slip away. As Gilbert advises, it had "arrived," powerfully and on its own timeframe.

Not so long ago I read the thoughts of poet David Whyte on this matter of despair in his ever-insightful book, *Consolations*. That first Thanksgiving night they seemed poignantly relevant.

> Despair is a necessary and seasonal state of repair...
> an internal physiological and psychological winter
> when our previous forms of participation in the
> world take a rest...It is the place we go when we
> do not want to be found in the same way anymore.
> Despair is the time in which we both endure and
> heal, even when we have not yet found the new
> form of hope.
>
> We take the first steps out of despair by taking
> on its full weight and coming fully to ground in
> our wish not to be here. In that place, strangely,
> despair cannot do anything but change into some-
> thing else, into some other season, as it is meant
> to do, from the beginning. Despair is a difficult,
> beautiful necessary.[4]

The six-hour drive back to Denver from Ghost Ranch gave me opportunity to ponder the question of whether I was thankful during this Thanksgiving season of 2016. The answer is a measured and sobered, "Yes, I am." The desert terrain and intense darkness, meager accommodations, overcast days, damp and drizzly nights, solitude, early morning hikes, Gilbert and Whyte, and the Spirit, all converged to reintroduce me to one of life's paradoxes: embracing current loss, grief, and even despair is the only pathway to true future joy.

10 | PLEASANT PLACES

THERE'S A SAYING in the ancient wisdom of the Hebrew scriptures that goes something like this: The boundary lines have fallen for me in pleasant places; surely I have a delightful heritage.[1] This psalm gives voice to that now-thought-to-be-antiquated belief that God is both good and personal. When Janene's sister and brother-in-law acquired fifty acres of beautiful and in every way pastoral Texas Hill Country land some years ago, they named it "Pleasant Places," in keeping with their persuasion that this refuge from Dallas life was indeed a gift from above.

Those fifty acres in the middle of nowhere Texas became a sanctuary for Janene and me, especially the return to her beloved Texas bluebonnet-covered terrain in the spring. That ranch house gladly contained hour upon hour of deep, soul-filling conversation for Janene with her dear sister whom she loved and cherished with all of her heart. There was the laughter and celebration of family reunions under the live oaks. Those long, early morning walks down Sandy Lane to B.H.'s 1970s trailer home for a pound of his homegrown pecans... priceless.

And that last May visit to Pleasant Places with Janene before dementia overtook her is so vivid in my mind's eye it seems like yesterday evening, not a several years old memory. Somehow that back porch at twilight with a cold Shiner's, the crickets and katydids in full chorus, a lone coyote's signal, and the whispering of a slight southern breeze all occasioned some of the most intimate conversations in our marriage.

With Janene's early adjustment to institutional living underway, I decided a week in the Hill Country would be good for my soul. The process of her separation from me and the transition to memory care had taken its toll on me and I was emotionally exhausted. Janene had overpowered the capacity of no less than four memory care facilities to manage her "exit seeking" and "eloping persistence." These are all industry specific and professional terms intended to dilute the reality for a spouse that their loved one is trying to run away and break out of the facility all day, every day at the beginning. The nice terms proved not to be all that helpful when after a few short weeks, yet another Director of Wellness called to say, "we are not equipped to take care of your wife at our facility." Putting a thousand miles between my now emotionally vacant home and Janene's placement events seemed just the ticket.

I settled into a nice routine at Pleasant Places but was ambushed by loneliness and grief once the quiet of Pleasant Places took effect. It had seemed that a few days of quiet in the Hill Country after an unusually busy travel and work schedule would be just what the proverbial doctor ordered.

But as soon as my mind and body relaxed, I was flooded with the loss of Janene and the person that she once was and the relationship we once had. Perhaps it was being in Austin and the shattered hope that she could join me to tour our favorite haunts from the earliest years of our marriage in this unique city. Or maybe it was that it seemed every couple I saw was in meaningful conversation and connection with each other... the kind I used to have with my soul mate and best friend.

I didn't fight the tears. They arrived at will. The flood of emotion came frequently and intensely. Seeing the waning blue bonnets, enjoying the Tex-Mex food, and absorbing the full moon over the live oaks in the Hill Country all seemed to point to the hole in my soul and the keen loss that FTD has created in my life. Grief hunts us down. It has a life of its own. Try as we may, it really can't be managed.

Do I feel that dementia destroyed my well-deserved get away? Not at all. In fact, quite to the contrary, it may well have given me a so-called jump start on the adjustment required to live the next season of my life reasonably well. On the lengthy drive back home to Denver from the Hill Country and through the vast reaches of West Texas it eventually dawned on me that the week alone at Pleasant Places helped me befriend a word and experience that heretofore I avoided at all costs: *brokenhearted*. The poet and ever insightful, David Whyte, makes these observations...

> Heartbreak is unpreventable; the natural outcome of caring for people and things over which we have no control. Heartbreak is how we mature... heartbreak may be the very essence of being human, of being on the journey from here to there...
>
> There is almost no path a human being can follow that does not lead to heartbreak.
>
> Heartbreak asks us not to look for an alternative path, because there is no alternative path.
>
> Realizing its inescapable nature, we can see heartbreak not as the end of the road or the cessation of hope...[2]

I'm wondering if you have a safe place, a place for you, a place where your soul is at home enough for you to meet and face the depth of your grief and heartbrokenness. It might be near the ocean, or mountains, or desert, or heartland, the beach, a nearby park, that favorite hike, an empty cathedral. It awaits your coming.

11 | PROVIDENCE

On most days I am still a firm believer in Providence. You see, early in life I found the concept of an all-caring, all-controlling God easy to accept… untested and true. Then too this belief was a natural extension of my idyllic environs, the kind that so many can only imagine—loving parents, strong extended family, the rhythmic agrarian lifestyle, fried chicken Sunday dinner with grandparents, the unconditional love of my collie Teddie, and all in the heartland of Iowa during the late 50s just before the cosmic egg had broken. It's not a demanding stretch to embrace the notion that there is a benevolent, personal Spirit who is working things out on my behalf when all is going well. When "all the stars seem aligned," both the young and old alike handily affirm that God, or The Universe as many say, lacks neither goodness nor power.

But it didn't take too long before my childhood belief in the

Providential got roughed up a bit. When my great aunt Alice died unexpectedly during her routine Sunday afternoon nap, my grandmother Hershberger came to live with us on the farm until she died one solemn, tearful Saturday evening. I can still hear the sound of what my mother called, "your grandma's death rattles." And then there was the heartbreak with a high school sweetheart, a miscarriage of Janene's first pregnancy after six months, my dear friend Jim killed by a drunk driver and leaving Mary Jane to raise three kids, my business partner and his 13-year-old son dying in a car accident, and so on. We all have our list. Even a not so intellectually curious farm boy eventually begins to raise the age-old questions of where was a loving God and why is the Universe conspiring against me in the midst of these heartbreaks.

This matter of Providence became all the more poignant for me when my wife, an accomplished RN/MBA, entrepreneur and author, was diagnosed with early onset dementia at age 59 in the prime of her life and career and became a memory care resident at age 65.

When I reflect on the enormity of the gap between the aspirations for our family that my three daughters, sons-in-law, and I once had and our current reality, it is staggering. Our situation is only one amongst the plethora of ways folks find their lives ambushed by some form of painful, in some cases, obscenely tragic intrusions of what appears to be a senseless, capricious Plan B that must now be lived.

I have listened to hundreds of people say over the years

when in the throes of the early accommodation to Plan B: "Well, if there is a loving and all-powerful God, He sure is asleep at the wheel."

If you are among the precious few for whom life has worked out as you thought it would, try to understand that some of us identify with author Anne Lamott who writes that her prayer in the face of suffering is sometimes a simple "Really?" When life is spinning out of control and the notion of Providence seems but a naïve, childhood memory, then "Really?" is at the very least an honest expression of the brokenheartedness that we cannot escape in the face of the incomprehensible.

It's not by accident that we strain and stretch for control and celestial puppeteer metaphors to make a modicum of sense out of the seemingly impossible conundrum. Our inability to lean into ambiguity and mystery, our propensity to keep asking "why?" and especially "why me?", and the ever-present need for cause and effect explanations can cause any of us to do some pretty remarkable intellectual and spiritual gymnastics at times. Dualistic, black and white thinking seems always ready and available for the faint of heart who demand quick and easy answers.

And then there are those numbing, one-dimensional attempts to simplify what the best minds in the world have struggled with for centuries. Here is a recent example from a well-known spiritual leader putting forward a definition of Providence: "Providence means that the hand of God is in the glove of human events. When God is not at the steering wheel, He is the backseat driver. He is the coach who calls the signals from the bench. Providence is the unseen rudder on the ship. God is the pilot at the wheel during the night watch."

I will leave to the theologians and philosophers the task of nuancing intellectual and spiritual dilemmas this anthropomorphic view of Providence creates. Quite frankly though, this definition of Providence is no more helpful to me than my New Age friends' admonition that "It's all good," or the agnostic who is certain chance and fate govern our lives in an impersonal and mechanistic universe.

What I need is a working definition of Providence that actually helps me lean into the essence of daily life without a partner and soulmate. A notion of Providence that fits with the complexity of life as it is now would be nice. I would like a durable Providence that fortifies my spiritual bench strength and capacity to embrace the daily polarities of grief and gratitude, pain and pleasure, sorrow and satisfaction, joy and suffering.

As I reflect on this matter of Providence, I am 35,000 feet over Nebraska on a business trip to none other than Providence, Rhode Island. Must be coincidental.

I wondered how this historic city and purveyor of the finest New England clam chowder might have come upon its name. I discovered a story embedded in this history that helps inform a functional definition of this word that has become so important to me in the wake of my wife's progressive neurological disorder for which there is neither treatment nor cure. Here it is in its briefest form.

The winter of 1635 was cold even by New England standards for young Roger Williams, the staunch Baptist who was seeking a new home since his belief in the separation of church and state had left him exiled from the Massachusetts Bay Colony. He was walking along the coastline south of Boston when the Native American chief Massosoit [sic] found him and eventually gave Williams shelter from the severe winter conditions and brought him to his own home near the present-day town of Bristol, Rhode Island. That spring Massosoit [sic] gave Williams a tract of land along the Seekonk River in what is now known as East Providence. As an expression of his gratitude and his faith Williams describes his naming of the town in this way…

…having made covenant of peaceable neighborhood with all the natives around us, and having a sense of God's merciful provision in my distress, I decided to call the place Providence. I desired that it might be a place of shelter for persons distressed…[1]

"A sense of God's merciful provision in my distress." Now there is a durable, time-honored definition that encourages and helps me face another day. Having been literally thrown out in the cold by his fellow Brits in our colonial times for a belief that was to become a foundational tenant of the new country, Williams did not become cynical and jaded. He was able to see the hand of God in the kindness of Chief Massasoit in the midst of his trouble.

I find this example of Williams' attitude in the face of hardship and his founding of Providence instructive. He certainly could have blamed his fellow colonialists for his dilemma that winter of 1635. He could have felt sorrow for himself and succumbed, as we all can at times, to some form of powerlessness and victimhood. Blaming an all-powerful God for neglect has its appeal. Williams might even have refused the outstretched hand of the Native American chief, acting on that exaggerated and ever-tempting view of our autonomy and self-reliance. I suspect Williams had developed a stance toward life that helped him see a merciful provision when it occurred. Perhaps he had developed the eyes to see the unpredictable and serendipitous.

Intellectuals, commoners, and folks from all walks of life have written volumes about, debated, and discussed the topic of Providence for centuries. But in the final analysis it matters not what they all believe or want us to believe, you and I have to decide in what or whom we believe about how and why things happen as they do. Try as we may to ignore the matter when in the flow, life has a way of not letting us off this particular personal and existential hook.

I do wonder though, if on many more occasions than I want to admit, Providence reaches down into the very fabric of my completely ordinary life and gives me just the spiritual lift I need.

12 | DAY BY DAY

I was on my return from a long, maybe even epic, road trip I had taken to Glacier Park, Banff, and Lake Louise. For me, this was the first such trip to be undertaken completely alone. The beauty of the Canadian Rockies is stunning, even for those of us who live in the Colorado expression of these Rockies. But they were not so stunning as to dull my awareness that I had the extravagant privilege of enjoying creation's majesty while my wife was institutionalized in the confines of a secure memory care facility with a community of 20 others whose atrophied minds are now housed in bodies that continue to function day after unrelenting day. I was alone, as was she.

While traveling south on Highway 165 through the massive rolling hills of wheat north of Moscow, Idaho, late in the day, I spotted what appeared to be a classic country church about a half-mile to my right. The dusk sunlight made me question if it was in fact what I imagined it to be. I turned off on the next gravel road and came upon one of those enormous, dust-shrouded harvesters inching its way through the golden field silhouetted by the late day sun, thinking to myself, *I sure hope it's a John Deere.* No thought would seem more insignificant unless you had grown up with a father who was "a John Deere man" and spent your childhood a stone's throw away from Waterloo, Iowa, the home of Deere manufacturing in the 1960s.

It turned out not only to be a 9950 John Deere combine with its enormous 30-foot header, but it was operated by Duane Cunningham, a local farmer who shut the machine down, walked over to my car and asked this complete stranger and Iowa farm boy if he wanted to ride with him in the combine for a while.

After a lengthy conversation in Duane's air-conditioned cab regarding the glaciation of Idaho's panhandle, agrarian family businesses, unwelcome government intrusions, and wheat prices, I got refocused on whether the country church I thought I had spotted from the highway was there.

I soon discovered it was not a figment of my imagination. Not but 300 yards away I found Freeze Community Church, a country church in all of its primitive beauty with the fading sunlight touching the nearby gravestones.

Of course, it was unlocked there in the security of its agrarian environment. And the moment I opened the weather-beaten doors I recognized I had entered sacred space.

I sat in the back pew to quiet myself and absorb for a timeless moment. I became keenly aware of my heartbroken aloneness, the impossibility of getting closure to my loss, the countless ways my life had changed since Janene left our home, the deep sorrow on the faces of our daughters, the prospect of an indefinite future without a life companion, and the longing for some tangible evidence of comfort.

Concurrent with these cascading thoughts of my struggle I was flooded with gratitude for the road trip I was so remarkably fortunate to have completed, the grandeur of the Rockies, the privilege of vacation, multitudes of supportive friends, daughters and family who love me well, long-time parishioner friends who are not afraid to look dementia in the eye, a home that has become a sanctuary for me, neighbors who care, and even my dramatically productive garden this year. Here again grief and gratitude, pain and pleasure, joy and sorrow, blessing and suffering could embrace each other in the reverence of this remote and sacred place of worship for that faithful band of wheat farmers who make their way here each Sunday, and for even me, the solitary interloper from afar.

And then I heard The Voice... the one you have heard on rare occasions too... the hunch, intuition, urge, nudge, sometimes audible, the unexpected thought, usually cryptic, but always perfectly clear. This time it said simply, "Go up to the piano and look at the hymnal."

I walked down the center aisle between the ten rows of well-worn oak benches on each side and made my way to the left and up to the old upright piano only to find the hymnal open to page 299 and the hymn "Day by Day." The words were penned in 1865 by the Swedish hymn writer Carolina Sandell-Berg several years after she witnessed the tragic drowning death of her father. The lyrics were obviously born out of a time of grief and human distress, not totally unlike yours and mine as we navigate our way through the challenges of our own unwelcome and sometimes excruciatingly painful current reality.

I sat down on the neatly embroidered piano bench in the silence of the rolling wheat fields, attempting to break down these lyrics, getting beyond the old English wording and romanticized language to the essence of their message.

As tears flowed I knew without reservation that through the glimpse of the church steeple, the right turn, the John Deere, the farmland sunset, the country church, the silence, The Voice, and hymn #299... the Providential heart that is kind beyond all measure found a way to make it unmistakably clear to this grieving and grateful soul that merciful provision is available in my distress, and yours too, my friend.

Day by Day and with each passing moment,
Strength I find to meet my trials here;
Trusting in my Father's wise bestowment,
I've no cause for worry or for fear.
He whose heart is kind beyond all measure
Gives unto each day what He deems best.

Lovingly, it's part of pain and pleasure,
Mingling toil with peace and rest.

Every day the Lord himself is near me
With a special mercy for each hour;
All my cares He fain would bear, and cheer me,
He whose name is Counselor and Power.
The protection of His child and treasure
Is a charge that on Himself He laid;
As thy days, thy strength shall be in measure,
This the pledge to me He made.

Help me then in eve'ry tribulation
So to trust Thy promises, O Lord,
That I lose not faith's sweet consolation
Offered me with Thy holy word.
Help me, Lord, when toil and trouble meeting,
E'er to take, as from a father's hand,
One by one, the days, the moments fleeting,
'Till I reach the promised land.[1]

13 | HER DEAR SOUL

IT OUGHT NOT TO have felt as intrusive and violating as it did, since she had been in the memory care facility for a year, I told myself. Janene was never coming home. She would never warm our bed again. There would be no more pillow talks. Those personal, functional, daily life agreements good enough marriages have were now obsolete in the face of her poignant absence. Her thoughts of us, of her love, of deepest desires, of shared intimacies were now forever imprisoned in a mind ravaged by a form of dementia that robs even brilliant minds like hers of the capacity to retrieve the words that once so eloquently expressed the nuances of her generative heart and intellect. With all my rational, common sense applications, it still felt a little "weird" as we say, to be reading her journal. But as so often is the case, if we persevere through the dissonance, relinquish control, no longer require redemption to take our preferred forms, and trust the moment, there is a life-giving gift to be found.

It started out as yet another one of those necessary and utilitarian tasks a caregiver is required to perform when a loved one is institutionalized… simply cleaning out her bedside stand. A step of relinquishment and letting go that is rarely made easier by procrastination. Necessity and utility eventually overcame the resistance to deal with her things, personal effects, and yes, even her journals, that expressed the deepest matters of her soul and whose privacy we had so carefully respected and protected over 40-plus years spent together. I naively waded into what I assumed would be a 10-minute task and I would then proceed with my Saturday to-do list. It was not to be.

Since Janene was a bit of a hoarder I was not surprised to see an old pair of socks she would slip on when her feet got cold in bed, a few well-sculpted ear plugs to block my snoring, numerous to do lists, and then at the bottom of the drawer one of her journals from no less than two decades ago. Breaking our agreement to never read each other's journals on the sly, I skimmed and scanned through her beautiful handwriting and came upon her entry for January 30, 1997, our anniversary date. My soul was deeply stirred by what I found, and surprised that in all of our conversations over the past 20 years about our life together and our future, Janene had never spoken these words to me. She was never one to hold back her thoughts and affirmations.

It seems to me that there are particular songs that musicians perform, crucial clutch situations in which athletes excel, moments of extraordinary challenge to which leaders rise, things said at the rituals of great joy and tragedy, responses to crises large and small in the warp and woof of life that in some way make explicit the character and identity of an individual. They define who we really are. Janene's few sentences tucked away for those 20 years expressed on our 27th anniversary unmistakably bear witness to the essence of this exceptional woman and presented an invigorating challenge for me to meet in the face of our radically redefined relationship.

But here is what touched my heart about Janene in that anniversary journal entry and turned my routine housecleaning chore into hours of reflection and gratitude. She was a woman of deep faith, quick to recognize the activity of God in the most personal experiences of life. She was capable of both rich self-observation and keen awareness of the other. Expressed gratitude was a spontaneous and natural expression of her heart before the encroachment of dementia. She was what we now call a life-long learner. She nurtured and encouraged her own growth and mine and was not threatened by either.

So now on this anniversary day, and even though we can no longer celebrate together, I will celebrate the author of these words and the enormity of her contribution to me, our family, and her circle of influence.

January 30, 1997
"Our 27th anniversary! I am so thankful for all

these years with Jay. Credit goes to God and the commitment He's inspired within us, and our commitment to grow and accept each other's growth. I really love who he is and who he is becoming. And even if he became nonfunctional, I would just love his dear soul."

And then there is that last sentence which took my breath away, moved me to tears, and presented this foreshadowing of things to come in our lives with one theatrical twist. It was she who became "nonfunctional" and I who am now asked to "just love her dear soul." My hope and prayer is that I will be equal to the task. However imperfectly, and with an informed humility that this disease requires of my caregiving, may I offer to Janene the love and persevering spiritual support that I know she would have provided for me were our roles reversed.

14 | HOLY GROUND

DURING THE EARLY stage of my adjustment to Janene's placement in memory care, I found myself in the presence of three extraordinary men. One had just weathered two heart attacks that put him in a 1% survival category according to his surgeon who fixed his "widow maker." Another had just buried his 27-year-old son who finally lost a decade-long battle with drug addiction. And the third was struggling to support a son of 29 who was recently diagnosed with MS. After my lengthy and gut-wrenching monologue attempting to describe the stark reality that Janene was never coming home again, I simply ran out of words. I sat in a silent, heartbroken, grief-stricken stupor. And then a stunningly rare thing happened.

Nothing.

These three men with nine shared decades of accumulated wisdom and life experience said not a word. They simply maintained powerful eye contact with me. Silence. No advice given. Nothing trite said. No New Age, Buddhist, or Christian clichés. No words of encouragement. It was an eloquent silence. Finally, one man uttered these poignant words: "We are standing on holy ground."

I am not the first to ponder this matter of silence, stillness, and the holy. Maria Popova observes in her ever-insightful blog, *Brain Pickings:*

> Even when nothing is happening, something is happening. This is a difficult fact for the human animal to fathom—especially for us modern sapiens who so ardently worship at the altar of productivity…[1]

What I discovered while sitting in a wordless vacuum with these men is that silence, doing nothing, actually is a powerful form of communication. There was a comfort, camaraderie, a brotherhood these men offered me in the form of this silent container for my grief, which, at that moment, words would have diluted.

I am reminded of the authenticity and vulnerability of my father's beloved and long-time pastor, Robert Yoder, the morning after my mother's shockingly unexpected death. The final chapter of my dad's life was heartbreakingly and unalterably changed overnight, literally. I was witness to the first and only thing this man of the cloth, biblical scholar, and dear friend said when we three met in Dad's apartment the morning after Mom's death, "Clark, I have no idea what to say."

My father's response was an equally poignant statement, "Well, I don't either."

So they wept together. I suspect that at times tears and wordlessness are a good resource for the unrelenting road ahead.

While battling stage 4 cancer at age 30-something with a good marriage, healthy two-year old, and Duke University professorship, Kate Bowler finishes her book, *Everything Happens for a Reason: And Other Lies I've Loved*, with this bit of advice...

> Silence. The truth is that no one knows what to say. It's awkward. Pain is awkward. Tragedy is awkward. People's weird, suffering bodies are awkward. But take the advice of one man who wrote to me with his policy:
>
> Show up and shut up.[2]

I wonder why we whisper in the galleries when viewing the works of Monet, or Rembrandt, or Russell. Why did I tear up when the pipe organ began to play, echoing into the chambers of the Gothic Cathedral of Cologne Germany several summers ago? In the summer of 1962, why did a hush fall on our rural Iowa farmhouse where my grandmother Hershberger was living her last day? Why at the Vietnam Memorial Wall in Washington, is there a palpable reverence and riveted awe?

It seems there is a universal intuition that informs us when we are standing on holy ground for any number of reasons… artistic, spiritual, architectural, celebratory, tragic, sacred, or poignant. We all have life tipping points, strategic decisions, before and after moments in our lives that shape our direction and destiny. Some are unavoidably obvious, some are somewhat camouflaged, and others might be hidden, but right in plain view. I wonder if we have eyes to see.

There is a nuance in the archetypal and iconic Hebrew story of Moses and the burning bush in which it is said that, "Moses turned aside to see why the bush was not burnt by the fire." He recognized the highly improbable. He stopped. He observed. He had a willingness to look deeper. And, he listened. It was only then that he heard The Voice asking him to make a transition from sheepherder to emancipator of his people. And as you may recall, it was this same Voice that invited Moses to "take off your sandals, for the place you are standing is holy ground."

Don't you wonder how often you and I have failed to deeply observe the "coincidental," those large and small events of life that sometimes refute explanation? We've been in a hurry, of course. We are too often addicted to the business drug. We are on an important mission, say to pick up a six-pack. Whatever. How often might I have missed the deeper meaning, failed to slow my pace, left my sandals or boots on, stomping right on through the holy ground that was pregnant with emotional and spiritual growth? I want to travel through life with loosely buckled sandals just in case I run across a burning bush that needs investigation.

I am reminded of a line in an old hymn that attempts to depict this dance between the physical and spiritual worlds.

We are standing on holy ground,
For I know that there are angels all around.[3]

Might those three dear friends of mine well have been "angels"? Well, what I do know is they had the spiritual and emotional capacity to discern where I was and where the four of us were—on holy ground. They held what some call essential silence, offering me the opportunity to go a little deeper, to find another level of acceptance in my own grief.

15 | THE LOST RING

As so frequently happens in memory care facilities with resident valuables, Janene's wedding band came up missing. This loss was duly reported by the staff the next morning. Of course, no one knew what had happened. These facilities always have custodial family members sign documents that absolve the institution of all responsibility if your loved one loses a valuable item—one of the more ingenious ways to protect from the potential moral failure of staff in the middle of the night. In any case, and certainly without proof of staff indiscretion, Janene's sister and I turned her room upside down to no avail. This inexpensive, simple gold band that I purchased just off Congress Avenue near the University of Texas in Austin in 1970 has been a constant reminder and symbol of the love and commitment between the two of us through good seasons and tough times in our marriage. It was the sentimental value, not that it was a piece of fine jewelry, that tugs at my heartstrings.

Janene loved to garden. After proudly presenting her harvest of green beans to me one summer morning, I noticed this band—that was now mysteriously missing in the memory care unit—was missing that morning as well. She was terribly upset. After an inch by inch scrutiny of our bathroom, bedroom, and closet the ring was nowhere to be found. The garden was our last hope of finding it. And sure enough, the tiniest sparkle of gold in the Colorado sunshine amongst the bush bean leaves caught my eye. Janene was delighted, we hugged in the bean patch, and a sweet conversation ensued of how loved she felt when first she wore the ring and how "to this day I'm so proud to wear it." The ordinary, material stuff of this life can take on such deep and heartfelt meanings.

So my sister-in-law and I made our way to none other than the nearby Walmart jewelry department, laughing all the way that Janene, if she could, would have been pleased we were being so frugal and also how we both had spent more than a few hours berating this big box store over the years for the kitsch it sold and how it had destroyed the historic mom and pop general store across small town America. The lady in charge of the jewelry department quickly said they had no gold or silver bands.

Now here is where the event gets interesting. I will simply report what happened and you can come up with your own interpretation.

I felt nudged to look at their case of rings regardless of her disclaimer. And there, front and center in full view was a sterling silver band for a whopping $38. And, wouldn't you know, it also turned out to be Janene's exact size. The clerk retorted, "I wonder where that came from." My thoughts went back to Roger William's definition of Providence, and the reason he named the fine Rhode Island town by that name back in the severe winter of 1635... "A sense of God's merciful provision in a time of distress."

So we made our way back to Janene's memory care facility with our providential treasure, wondering if she would recall its significance, knowing explanation was no longer a possibility, and hoping we would not run headlong into that faraway look in the eyes of a dementia sufferer when they cannot comprehend and yet somehow know they lost the capacity to do so. It's a painful moment with a loved one.

Now understand the current level of Janene's functioning. She can no longer read. This devoted fitness lady only sits or walks to the dining room. Her walk is now the characteristic ALZ shuffle. Her vocabulary is down to a precious few words. And her nonsensical sentences of two or three words are repeated over and over. There remain several insoluble sentences that give expression to the affirming person she once was, like, "You're so beautiful." She spends her day resting on her bed, eating meals, and sitting in the activity room. Her once vibrant and razor sharp, racing mind is reduced to at best a snail's pace. She is, as some would rightfully and bluntly say, a mere shell of the person she used to be.

So it was for good reason Janene's sister and I were not sure what to expect at best and worried that the effort to replace the lost ring would be yet another one of the futile attempts to restore a reality, a former life experience, and relationship that the disease has stolen. Would we be required to both confront and accept another level of loss and relinquish it at the hands of this mysterious and unpredictable disease?

Janene was seated on her bed as we entered the room so I knelt beside her, opened the little box, and pointed to the wedding band. She instantly smiled, laughed, pointed to my band, and began repeating her perseverative phrases with intense and heartfelt expressiveness. Then she wrapped her arms around my neck and we hugged. For a few fleeting seconds, we were transposed back to St. David's Episcopal Church overlooking Lake Travis just west of Austin a half century ago at twilight where she so excitedly accepted my proposal and ring.

Those suggesting Janene is no longer there, that dementia has robbed her of all personhood and identity might well have knelt along with me at her bedside had they been privileged to witness an experience that transcends physiology or scientific inquiry. A mystery is not something about which we know nothing. It is a reality, a circumstance in which our understanding and our knowledge is incomplete. And there are times when kneeling is the only appropriate response.

16 | WILL SHE KNOW ME?

EVERY PERSON WHOSE life is closely and fatefully linked to a loved one suffering from dementia or Alzheimer's wonders when the day will come when their brother, sister, mother, dear friend, father, wife, or husband will no longer recognize them. We dread the moment when that most primitive of all connections, the interpersonal bridge that may well have been strong for decades, is stolen by the unrelenting, onward march of the debilitating and progressive disease.

That day came for our family when my three daughters and I visited their mother two years after she became a resident in a secure memory-care facility. She did not recognize her three loving, engaging, beautiful, and articulate adult girls whom she has adored for decades and who were the source of a deep, maternal pride.

Now this might be understandable under the worst of

physical or psychological circumstances, say after an accident, surgery, or mental breakdown if a young woman had not been committed or attached to her children. But Janene could not have enjoyed mothering more. She looked forward to becoming pregnant and unlike many women, absolutely loved how she felt while carrying a child. Her normally upbeat and energetic personality was all the more so when with child. Every stage of infant and child development accessed her extraordinary drive for understanding and excellence—nursing, infancy, toddlerhood, language acquisition, physical and intellectual challenges, athletic pursuits, normal orneriness, discipline, individual differences—they all became the focus of her attentive motherhood. She refused to turn over the total care and keeping of her young girls to daycare and maintained a balance of part-time professional effort as an RN/MBA and time with her children. After reading a child development text when our oldest daughter was not but two years old, Janene simply said, "I refuse to miss any of our girl's developmental benchmarks because of work."

It was simply mindboggling, in spite of our awareness and considerable knowledge of dementia, to actually witness it happening. How does one get their mind wrapped around being with a mother who is there physically, but who also is psychologically, interpersonally, and verbally compromised so profoundly?

So for Janene to have that now too familiar glazed and struggling to comprehend look in her eyes when she saw all of her daughters together after a one year hiatus was heart-breakingly difficult. We all knew what had just happened, and we all held it together emotionally at the time and made our way back to a little sunroom where the staff had set up a nice lunch for the five of us.

What came to mind as we gathered in that little sunroom was an exacting question asked by our youngest daughter of Dr. Bruce Miller, director of the University of California at San Francisco Center for Memory and Aging and the leading researcher in America on Frontotemporal Dementia at the time of Janene's diagnosis.

"If Mom does not recognize a word or a person is it helpful to tell her what it means or who the person is?"

After a poignant pause Dr. Miller responded with the kindest look on his face, "That is a very good question, but there is no research evidence to suggest that once a word or a person is lost from your mother's memory that it can be recovered."

It was with this awareness that my heart began to pound and my thoughts race, anticipating how painfully long our visit with Janene was likely to be.

More than a little bewildered and disoriented, my three daughters and I attempted to navigate an impossible situation and conversation with a wife and mother who had lost the mental capacity to recognize the three people into whose lives she had poured her own, whose strong minds and wills had challenged hers, and for whom she had prayed and sacrificed countless times.

Hundreds of thousands in America alone have and are experiencing this tragic moment when dementia and ALZ lacerates the heart and fabric of life-giving relationships that are at the foundation of human flourishing. It leaves one bludgeoned emotionally when familial reality as we have known it is rearranged in one stunning and unexpected moment.

As this new reality began to set in for me, an equally and stunningly encouraging thing happened in that sunroom to which I was a front row observer. One of our daughters, in an act of brilliant emotional and social intelligence, got up from her chair, walked around our little lunch table, knelt beside her mom, and began to hug and kiss, her mother. Then gently rubbing and caressing her mother's arm, she kept repeating one word over and over, "Mama, Mama, Mama, Mama" for an uncomfortably long time.

And then the neurologically inexplicable happened.

Janene recognized her daughter.

Unable to retrieve her daughter's name from her dementia-ravaged temporal lobe, she simply moaned, groaned, smiled, and then kissed her daughter on the lips while the light and sparkle of recognition came back to her big blue eyes as she said, "oh, Oh, OH, OH" more loudly with each repetition. Had Dr. Miller been in the room, I am certain his eyes would have welled up with tears too as we stood in awe of how the miracle of love, touch, and tenderness bypasses the scientifically and neurologically impossible when we might least expect it.

Then Janene pointed to each of us and counted, "One,

two, three, four, five," and laughed from the bottom of her soul. Though she was not able to say our names, she knew in her heart that she was in the loving embrace of her dear daughters and husband.

I am reminded of a story told by Francis Schaeffer, the Swiss philosopher and apologist for the supernatural in his book *The God Who Is There*. He was over the Atlantic when the engines stopped on his plane and after several plunging and terrifying minutes the engines started again, bringing all safely to the United States. When all had calmed down, his agnostic seatmate eventually asked Dr. Shaeffer why he thought the engines righted themselves and why they were not all lost at sea. His response to the philosophic question that the brightest and best minds have wrestled with for centuries was simple.

"Because I prayed and asked God to start them."[1]

A tenet of Schaeffer's thought was that we are not living in what he called "a closed universe" untouched by the supernatural, and that we live with the impenetrable mystery of when, how, and for what reason our otherwise rational existence is required to contend with the incalculable in our everyday lives. I am of the persuasion that on that day at 12:10 p.m. in the New Dawn Memory Care cottage on Blackhawk Street in Denver, we had one such moment in real time and space. I am grateful to have witnessed it in the most intimate and meaningful of circumstances and relationships.

17 | A LOPSIDED CLOSET

My three daughters continue to support and encourage me since their mother was diagnosed with dementia. They come from out of town to visit regularly. "Just want to see how you're doing, Dad" calls are frequent. There are more texts. They have shown up during times of intense transition, like when Janene was carted off to the emergency room by the county sheriff or when she was battling the new and unprecedented constraints of institutionalization. So when the three girls offered to clean out Janene's side of our walk-in closet on a recent visit it seemed like an ordinary enough next step of letting go. After all, Janene had been in the memory care facility for well over a year by that time.

But as it turned out, this gesture of tangible support from my daughters proved to be yet another one of the intense tipping points along this journey of grief and adjustment to the departure of my dear friend. After a decade plus of relinquishing, letting go, and conceding to the disease as graciously as I could, common sense would have advised that I wouldn't be surprised by another dimension of the loss. Loss has a limitless treasure trove of nuances and surprises around the next bend in the road.

So when these dear daughters of mine, after they'd finished their task of tending to their mother's side of the closet, wanted "just a girls' night out in downtown Denver," I gladly consented and headed upstairs to my now lopsided closet to get ready for bed and to be immersed in my latest good read.

Upon entering our little walk-in closet my eyes absorbed for the first time one more intrusion of this dreaded disease. I tried to catch my breath and then sank to my knees sobbing.

I puzzled a good bit over the depth and intensity of my emotional reaction to such an ordinary and reasonable event. How could I have been ambushed once again by this grief that has been a constant companion for over a decade? I tried to tell myself it was just clothing, shoes, and the ordinary stuff of life, not Janene that I no longer encountered during our morning and evening ritual. Long gone were the playful closet moments we both enjoyed with the tender touches, timely compliments, and intentional bumps at the various stages of our dressing and undressing daily rituals.

So why this breathtaking grief? How many waves of immobilizing emotions are yet to come? Was I overly attached to those outward, tangible remains of my wife and our life together? Were those clothes and personal effects evidence of some enshrined, weirdly sacred space I was unwilling to relinquish to the power of this disease that had changed our lives forever? Are the ordinary, tactile, material, and concrete things that make up our daily life still that important to me?

Then a very old and always relevant book came to mind entitled *A Place for You*, by Swiss psychiatrist Paul Tournier. He maintains that we are built to make meaningful and significant connections to our surroundings and the material world in which we find ourselves. We all need a place. We all must find a place that is grounding and reassuring in the midst of the whirlwind of contemporary life, Tournier affirms. He writes that the detachment from place and the material stuff of life advocated by some religious perspectives is not helpful, especially during times of transition.

Tournier's brilliant observation about this relationship we all have with the material world is an essential dimension of who we are. He makes it clear that:

> Man is not a pure spirit…he is bound up with matter, with things, with the ground he lives on. Our place is our link to the world. All the places we have lived in remain with us, like pegs in a vast storehouse, on which our memories are hung. Places of hurt and places of consolation, places of menace and places of reassurance, places of crying and singing—we preserve them all within us. My

place consists of the things I incorporate into my person—the suit in which I feel at ease or the tie that a friend gave me. For a woman there is the dress that flatters her figure…her rings, her necklaces.

A woman's handbag and a man's pockets are places that belong to their real lives! At every moment of our lives an ineffaceable network of correlations is being set up between our inner world and the external world. Nothing happens in pure abstraction.[1]

So that pink sweater she loved to wear because "people say I look so good in it"; the navy blue business suit she sported on the way to banker meetings as a corporate financial analyst; the threadbare nightgown that portrayed her reluctance to spend money on herself; the Colorado indigo sky silk blouse that made those Texas-sized blue eyes pop; the hiking shorts she wore to the summit of Colorado 14ers, the tired blue jeans that her sister Georgeann helped her find in Dallas; that pink ski jacket she wore as we skied down through the clouds off the peak of Mt. Verner at Steamboat Springs years ago… they weren't simply discards stuffed into garbage bags and deposited at the local Goodwill. They were the artifacts of the life Janene and I once lived and relished together. They were tangible symbols and links of meaning between our inner world and our external world. It was the joy, love, frustration, adventure, anxiety, the intimacy, and yes, the very meaning and memories of our four decades of shared living that were now missing. The absence of these icons of our former life is what so unexpectedly brought me to my knees when I saw the empty side of our closet for the first time.

On most days I am gracious with myself when the unexpected wash of grief comes once more on this road of the long goodbye. My mind reassures me that the emotion is triggered by necessary endings. This is the normal process of grief and eventual healing.

On bad days, well... it can be energy sapping self-incrimination that grief still has such sway on my life after more than a decade to adjust. Or some variation of an adolescent admonition as in, "Come on man, get over it already."

But what helps me gain my emotional and spiritual equilibrium again in the face of the inevitable turbulence of loss, is the counsel of mentors like Tournier. They remind me that, whether it's an unsuspecting smell, sight, sound, taste, or lopsided closet that occasions my brokenheartedness, that's what it means to be fully human. We are built to connect deeply with the stuff of both the intangible and the tangible world. And I will be forever grateful Janene and I lived not only a hearty spiritual life together, but we were fully bound up with matter as well. Hiking, biking, camping, amateur "foodies," homebodies, lovers, cocreators of three marvelous girls we were. For us it was both Heaven and Earth. I wouldn't trade that life with her for anything, even if its absence brings me to my knees.

18 | MY GIFT ON HER BIRTHDAY

It happened right in the middle of our now difficult conversations in which Janene struggles to put together a five- or six-word sentence, she spoke a perfectly lucid and stunning sentence on this her 67th birthday. This singular sentence in an otherwise painful visit to her memory care facility brought me a "peace which passes all understanding." It truly was a gift to this soul-weary companion of hers.

Now the phenomenon of occasional articulate communication is not terribly unusual amongst folks afflicted with Frontotemporal Dementia (FTD). But what made this sentence so stunning was Janene's totally uncharacteristic self-awareness, insight, and consequential thinking, the very things that FTD steals from the brightest of individuals like Janene and which she had not expressed in months, actually years, if I allow myself to acknowledge the pain of it all.

You see, one of the first cognitive and emotional intelligence functions to be lost with the advance of FTD is self-awareness—the capacity to recognize one's own emotional experience and describe it accurately. For years Janene insisted that there was nothing wrong even in the face of mounting evidence that words were becoming more difficult for her to retrieve and previously well-refined interpersonal skills were diminished, which friends and family were consistently reporting to me. She was certain no one could see the change and progression of the disease, insisting that I not talk to my family about it.

What makes FTD such a painful interpersonal and family disease is that it attacks the frontal lobe of the brain where personality, social decorum, self-management, and the whole range of life-enriching relationship skills are housed. It is a bizarre affliction that leaves even the most thoughtful children (and my three daughters certainly are) and spouses at a complete loss; some sort of interpersonal and familial quagmire with no operating manual.

So heartbreaking questions arise that in my pre-FTD life would never have been asked.

"Is this the person I married?"

"Did she actually say that?"

"Where did that extreme reaction come from?"

"How can Mom not know what 9/11 is?"

"How could she possibly not understand what I meant after 30 years of life together?"

Moments of intimacy and deep communication become

less frequent and eventually are completely absent as the disease progresses.

Those preciously unique moments that define a good enough marriage gradually are irretrievably lost as the disease makes its unrelenting advance. Nicknames. Our jokes. Spontaneous affection. Bad meals. Gourmet meals. Nights out. Unabashed candor. Accomplishments celebrated. Full moon. Knowing glances. Biking. Camping. Laughter. Worship. Deep conversation. These and countless other previously taken for granted meanings and moments that made up our everyday life together faded away like the twilight. I was no longer living with my soul mate, but instead a stranger had taken up residence in my dear friend's body and mind. It is the most heartbreakingly painful and excruciatingly protracted metamorphosis I have been called on to witness. And frankly, in all probability it is a long way from over.

There are more than a few spiritual struggles that have been thrust upon me in the last decade from my front row seat to Janene's agony and suffering. And agony may seem melodramatic, but not if you knew who she once was, not at all. The challenge for me that comes to mind is one Dante describes in his *Inferno* (now there is one dramatic poet) as he encounters the Virtuous Pagans on his journey toward Hell with his friend Virgil and finds that "they are not tormented, but their only pain is that they have no hope."[1]

No cure. No effective medication. No breakthrough research. No tips and tools. No help, basically. And all the professionals—bless their hearts, as my mother might have said—in an attempt to soften my reality describe the disease as "progressive"; a thoughtful euphemism meaning she will get worse and there is nothing the brightest and best researchers in the world can do about it.

I actually prefer what they used to say in Texas in the face of a life quandary: "Good luck to ya!" It's a Texan's soft, on the slant, way of saying, "It really sucks to be you and I love you anyway." This is all to say that the emotional and spiritual conundrum for those who love a dementia sufferer is a fertile seedbed for hopelessness and even despair.

Amongst the choices we don't get to make in life are the religious and spiritual orientation or demographic of the family into which we are born. Buddhist, atheist, agnostic, fundamentalist, evangelical, Republican, Democratic, rich, poor, urban or rural; we're pretty much stuck with it. And then there is the life-long process of coming to terms, or peace, or often finding our own pathway through the family of origin hand that we were dealt. And in my seventh decade of life, it seems it has taken most of a lifetime to accomplish this task. I've had my fair share of issues growing up in an ethnic, Christian, agrarian, close-knit, separatist, family business culture in the 1960s. And just a word of caution here… babies are worth saving, bathwater not so much.

For one thing, you never know when some artifact from that first family experience might come in handy, say when dementia, divorce, forest fire, illness, accident, or many forms of hardship find their way into your lives. A recent example is my running across a perspective embedded in the Christian sacred texts that addresses my psychological challenge with FTD, and Dante's hopelessness too for that matter. Here's how Saint Paul puts it after making the point that deep spiritual truth is housed in ordinary clay pots (we humans) …

> Therefore, we do not lose heart. Though outwardly we are wasting away, yet inwardly we are being renewed every day. For our light and momentary troubles are achieving for us an eternal glory that far outweighs them all. *[Whatever that means?]* So we fix our eyes not on what is seen, but what is unseen. For what is seen is temporal, but what is unseen is eternal.[2]

I think we all carry an intuitive awareness that values such as courage, kindness, commitment, grace, sacrifice, unconditional love, loyalty, faithfulness, forgiveness, forbearance, goodness, patience, and so on, are what endure. But in the face of the most daunting challenges and the proverbial perfect storm that life can sometimes bring our way, I am still tempted to lose my moorings and focus only on that which is fading away, namely my dear wife as I have known her in the past.

So on the days I can embrace the ancient wisdom of a fellow sojourner like Paul, I do quite well. There are a lot of "unseens" to focus on. There is no shortage of hope, faith, and love in my environment. I have a life to live, and it is a good one. And the truth be known, there is precious little I can actually do to ease Janene's pain or even more humbling, to companion her in the current loneliest journey of her otherwise good and often fulfilling life before FTD.

We will never know, but I sometimes wonder if Janene, since the loss of her seen world brilliance, manifested in spread sheets, details of life, and operational capacity, now lives most of her life in the unseen world. Her one lucid birthday line hints that might be the case.

Actually, aren't we all "wasting away"? Don't we all know that the seen, material world will not ultimately feed our souls? Haven't we all faced our own powerlessness in the face of an impenetrable life circumstance? And are there not times in life when all our brilliant strategizing, orchestrating, conceptualizing, masterminding, engineering, and even praying, all fall dramatically short?

Of course, there are many ways to think about Janene's moment of lucidity. And there are certainly more than a few possible interpretations—clinical, neurological, and otherwise. So make of these words whatever you will. This is simply a verbatim report of what she said to me between bites of her birthday cake.

But for me... it sparked hope for the future, comfort for the present, and encouragement to keep my eyes fixed on what matters most in the long run when Janene looked at me with now uncharacteristic clarity in those big blue eyes and said, "Jesus is taking care of me and my brain, and it makes all the difference."

19 | A STELLAR'S JAY

MY PRECIOUS MOTHER took her last breath at the snow-packed and icy intersection of Highway 1 and Larch Road just north of Washington, Iowa, the wintery morning of December 9, 1992, in an auto accident. She was in near perfect health for a woman of 85, so her unexpected death was a reverberating shock to our family and to her large network of friends. As an RN working in a local nursing home, Mom had accompanied many on the last leg of their journey from this life to the next. Aging, decline, suffering, Alzheimer's, hospice—none of it scared Mom. She knew how to befriend current reality.

So to honor Mom's spirit and capacity to "move toward the fire," on a visit back home not long after her death, it seemed timely that I should return to the scene of the accident, literally. It was part of my own coming to terms with the gaping hole in our family and the empty chair at the table during my occasional visits home. With a heavy, anxious, but determined heart, I made the brief ten-mile trip south from Kalona toward that fateful intersection where Mom came to the end of her journey.

It was early in the morning, quiet and sultry. A fine overcast, hot, humid heartland day was in the making. The normally busy Highway 1 was traffic free. I parked on the gravel road 100 feet west of the crossing and made my way back to this sacred intersection. It was then that my eyes met the gaze of an enormous red-tailed hawk sitting motionless on the southwest corner fence post, almost as if he had been waiting for my arrival. We held the connection for five stock-still seconds, and then he lifted off, soaring upward into the overcast heavenlies.

Some eight years later, a year after Dad joined Mom in their final resting place in the always pastoral setting of rural Iowa's Lower Deer Creek Mennonite Church Cemetery, I made another reflective trip to their graves to gain a measure of closure on my parents' departures. Picture the quintessential country graveyard. Silent. Rolling verdant hills. Hard wood timber borders the south fence. Full-throated meadowlarks. Blooming clover fields. Acre after acre of knee-high cornfields. The smells and sounds of a fertile countryside.

We Anglicans kneel at times of respect. So I found myself kneeling before Mom's and Dad's gravestones. The moment I did so, two Canadian geese, flying no more than 30 feet above the corn, came in view to my right and passed directly in front of me on their journey to the north.

Over a decade ago, Janene and I made a summer camping trip to Crestone, Colorado, that included the Nada Hermitage, a Carmelite retreat center with an arresting sculpture of the crucifixion above the chapel altar. This is no sweet Jesus dying a peaceful death on the cross. The rough wooden cross supports a metal representation of Christ writhing in pain, straining every muscle in his body to free himself from the torture. We sat in silence for an hour struggling to absorb the meaning and symbolism. Still speechless, we put on our shoes, mounted our mountain bikes and started down the path back to town. One hundred yards down the road from the chapel and not but 25 feet from the road stood a perfect, 10-point mule deer buck. His gaze was hauntingly penetrating as he stood transfixed and unmoving well inside the distance comfort zone of big game creatures of the wild. Janene and I reflexively slowed our bikes to a near stop and inched our way past his stare only to find him statuesque as we passed.

I spent last weekend with my three daughters in the magnificent beauty of Aspen, Colorado. We were in a reminiscent mood one evening around the campfire, fixing pocket stew, building the fire, and readying the s'mores, all keenly aware that one member of our small family was missing. When the pocket stew came off the fire and the fine wine was poured, we raised our glasses and toasted Janene, the originator of pocket stew and her untiring efforts of years gone by to make camping a memorable, fun experience for her three young girls and husband. At that very moment, as we honored our dear absentee, a stellar's jay with its characteristic black crested head and brilliant blue body caught our attention as it flew into our campsite and perched on an aspen limb right above us. Without hesitation, our youngest daughter said, "That's Mom."

We have all had first-hand or second-hand experience of the hard and brutal side of nature. Tornadoes, blizzards, floods, earthquakes, hurricanes, avalanches, and lightning, to name a few. In a multitude of ways, Mother Nature becomes less than maternal, ruthlessly destroying homes, families, and claiming the lives of innocent victims. At times the degree of devastation and the random nature of destruction's path brings us face-to-face with mystery and a plethora of unresolved questions.

And on the other hand, I've experienced along with you, this nurturing, healing, spiritual, comforting, and intensely personal interaction with creation; especially during turbulent seasons of my life. Sometimes this soft side of nature confronts my skeptical, rationally informed comfort zone much like the hard side does.

Well, so what do I make of these interactions with the birds and animals? Are they random chance coincidences? I just happened to be at the right place at the right time?

I was pondering these thoughts recently with a friend who reminded me of several lines from Elizabeth Barrett Browning, the prolific and influential British poet of the 19th century.

> *Earth's crammed with heaven,*
> *And every common bush aflame with God,*
> *But only he who sees takes off his shoes.*[1]

When Jesus was pressed to defend his consistent use of stories to explain spiritual mysteries and realities, Jesus' adherents seemed surprised to learn that some "get it" and some don't. Some hear and don't understand, and still others see but do not perceive. I wonder how often I, like those ancient skeptics, see and hear, but actually miss the deeper meaning of what is happening.

> May you and I be counted among that covey of devotees to whom it was said… But blessed are your eyes because they see, and your ears because they hear.[2]

20 | ONE PICTURE ONLY

From the very early and intermittent evidences that dementia had begun its unrelenting march to destroy Janene's extraordinary mind, I hoped and prayed she would live her last in our home.

Unlike many, she made it perfectly clear one evening after attending the housewarming of wealthy friends who had moved into their opulent, expansive, dream home, that she was content with ours. She loved the traditional "Denver box" we helped design and built together way back in 1985. The productive garden, big back yard, accessible bike trails, the remodeled kitchen, a view of Mt. Evans and Long's Peak, old cottonwoods, the quiet of our patio… all were home for Janene and she wanted nothing more. It was her place to be.

So when that fateful and unavoidable day finally arrived when she could no longer stay in her beloved surroundings, we tried to create a familiar setting in the sterile environs of a memory care facility room. C-3 in the east wing. Of course, it's impossible. But we tried.

This futile effort included clothes, bedspreads, books, CDs, a radio, an exercise bike, and a plethora of pictures that captured our lives as a couple and a family. These images were thoughtfully selected from a vast array of olden days slides, prints, and of course, our amazing wedding pictures, all of which we selected with a good bit of certainty that Janene would find them comforting reassurances of our love during those dreadfully difficult weeks of her initial adjustment to institutionalized life. Almost as an afterthought I grabbed a picture of Jesus that had hung in Janene's office for many years.

It seemed obvious enough to me that these visual reminders would connect Janene to multitudes of fond memories the two of us shared during the four precious years before our three girls began arriving on the scene, and then the mostly joy- and laughter-filled decades of their childhood.

I have spent 40 years helping folks adjust to life circumstances and challenges as a counselor, executive coach, and family business advisor. At least that's what I attempted to do. Many reported that I actually helped them navigate some of life's most challenging events. But as you know, there are people and situations that downsize and occasionally crush our sense of adequacy, agency, and efficacy regardless of our real or imagined history of stunning success.

Dementia is one of them.

I watched helplessly as Janene became what the memory care universe calls "exit seeking," "restless," and "adjustment challenged." I prefer our daughter's description of her mother's experience acclimating to the limitations of memory care living—torment.

In spite of the love and gifted calling among those who cared for Janene and her "family" of the dramatically compromised in the New Dawn Memory Care facility, it was an excruciatingly difficult time for her. She was eventually relieved only by the severe mercy of the progressing disease.

I was, for the most part, a bystander and front row observer to this process over which I had no control or influence and on which all my years of training and experience proved to be of little effect. I have fewer answers for the conundrums of life now, more humility though. I am better at just sitting with folks in pain. I can look mystery in the eye and not flinch or require a distraction.

In any case, I was shocked by the decors in her room on my first visit to see Janene mid-November of 2015 after the memory care staff recommended a two- week hiatus of no contact with her. (You see, the professionals believe it helps the dementia-afflicted person adjust to their new surroundings to not see loved ones and then assume they are there to take them home. Perhaps.) Much to my surprise all memorabilia and every family picture was nowhere to be found, including our prized wedding picture. The only artifact from her past to be found on her walls was the painting of Jesus which I had grabbed in haste on my way out the door.

Now this is no traditional painting of a sweet, blue-eyed, blond Jesus looking into the face of a gorgeous child on his lap. It depicts a focused, strong, determined Jesus with riveting eyes and compassionately handsome features. And the astonishing truth is the painting was completed by the child prodigy artist, Akiane Kramarik at the tender age of eight, while she was growing up in a non-religious home with atheist parents. She claims that at the age of three she began seeing visions of heaven and that Jesus appeared, telling her to capture what she saw in art form, which she began at the remarkable age of four.

This sort of childhood mysticism was no stranger to Janene. She had experienced it herself as a small child. Perhaps that's part of the reason the eight-year-old's work hangs alone in Janene's room.

Here are the bare essentials to a personal event Janene told to any spiritually curious person, without reservation and without variation, for well over 50 years. It was, as we say, all part of Janene's story.

At the age of six, her goldfish died, leaving this heart of hers that attached deeply broken and sad. She rode her bike to the Methodist church a few blocks away from their suburban Dallas home and entered the church, finding a seat near the back with her tearful face in her hands. After a few minutes she looked up and there was Jesus in the front of the church with this message for her first experience of loss, "I love you. I will take care of you. You have healing in your hands."

Be assured that the grownup Janene was not about to bifurcate her brilliant mind from the reality of these mystical experiences that continued throughout her adult life. There were more than a few visitations that came her way throughout our decades together and which we spent many deeply fascinating hours metabolizing in conversation. She was far too committed to intellectual honesty and disrespected what she called a "mindless faith" to let these parapsychological experiences go unexamined.

So not long after we met and then married in January of 1970, she devoured the likes of F. F. Bruce's *New Testament Documents: Are They Reliable?*, C. S. Lewis's *Mere Christianity*, Francis Schaeffer's *Escape from Reason*, and the William James classic, *The Varieties of Religious Experience*. Oh, how I miss her mind. On occasion it truly is a "suffocating loneliness," to borrow Henri Nouwen's term.

Maybe it was an initial emotional shock, but on further reflection not a surprise, to find only the one picture hanging in C-3 between the bathroom and the closet on the north wall. When I visit Janene in memory care, she always wants me to accompany her to C-3. Upon entering, without fail, I point to Akiane Kramarik's "Prince of Peace" work. And Janene's response, a twinkle in her eyes and a simple chuckle. No words. She no longer needs them to convey her truth.

On my 20-minute drive back home from this poignant visit with Janene, I got to wondering what singular picture might hang in my room if our roles in life were reversed. If I were stripped bare of my mind, my work, my recognition of dear family members, daily activities, freedom of movement, life-giving relationships, favorite foods, entertainment, home, agency of life, hobbies, productivity, known forms of worship, contact with nature, intimacy, and all that had previously defined me… what icon of identity and hope would Janene find in my room when she visits?

21 | HEARTBROKEN AND OPENHEARTED

I AM A HEARTBROKEN MAN. Truth be told, I've been heartbroken for well over a decade since my wife fell prey to this rare form of dementia that robbed her of an extraordinary capacity for intimacy and companionship. Janene was the quintessential soul mate before the disease made its camouflaged appearance and ambushed our marriage. She fed the heart and soul of a good marriage—not a perfect one, nor a happily ever after one either—but no longer. Now there is an ever-widening gap between my vibrant best friend of the past and the woman cooped up in a memory care facility. It is a heartbreaking gap.

In my remarkably protected youth, it seemed to me the heartbroken were crushed, defeated, and sometimes hopeless. They had lost their resilience—that capacity to bounce back when things go awry. Take for instance when our neighbor died back home in Iowa in a farm accident shortly after my

15th birthday. He rolled his 8N Ford tractor over while performing one of the most common and expected good farmer obligations in our agrarian community—mowing the roadside embankments on his property. Over coffee at the Chicken House, our local watering hole on Highway 22, it was said of his widow, "Fern is so heartbroken she'll never be the same." And to my youthful eyes, she never was.

Even for those blessed with some sort of golden touch, a gap inevitably appears between hopes, dreams, and the life we find ourselves living. It might be a calling to inner city education that proved too hard, a declined entry in the college of our choice, business failure, divorce, a marriage-threatening affair, a child's drug addiction, accident and tragedy in its many random and painful forms, mentally ill children, chronic illness, infertility, on and on. As we all know but still find difficult to digest when it comes, it's just a matter of *when*, not *if*, we will be plundered by loss. To love presupposes it will happen.

Of course, the list is endless, where normal dreams and hopes are either dashed or simply not realized, and we find ourselves in this heartbroken state with few guides and signposts to help us navigate our way through the uncharted territory. After all, how could I have prepared for the devastating impact of Frontotemporal Dementia in a partner with no genetic markers, no family history, and a razor-sharp mind? I had no narcissistic, overreaching expectation. I simply didn't want my wife to lose her mind. Not in her 50s anyway.

Parker Palmer, the Quaker educator and author, observes that heartbrokenness is the word to best describe this gap between my hopes and the current reality of Janene's disease and her absence. He believes there are two ways for our hearts to break when grief comes, unforgiving and unpredictable as it often does. They either break apart or they break open.[1]

We all know folks whose hearts have broken apart. They are angry, bitter, resentful, cynical, detached, brittle people who shatter easily or explode, lodging emotional shrapnel in the souls of their families, friends, employees, or spouses. You never know when or who will pull the pin that turns them into an angry grenade. Victims. Toxic. They project their pain and suffering indiscriminately and seemingly without much provocation. It's painful to watch and even more so to experience. They epitomize the Richard Rohr observation "that if we don't transform our pain, we will transmit it."[2]

My aunt almost got kicked out of her assisted living center for biting the nurses. Literally, sinking her teeth into the arms of the help. But before we hastily pass judgment… She contracted polio way back there before Dr. Salk, survived an iron lung, and then was plagued with chronic back pain for the next 70 years of her life. Unmarried and alone in an earlier era, she suffered socially as well as physically. And in the end, bless her dear tormented heart, it broke apart, not open.

We also know those dear ones whose heart has somehow broken open in the face of an irreparable gap. Mystery though it is, suffering transformed and enlarged their capacity to embody grace, mercy, understanding, kindness, and, indeed, love. They are a cadre of capacious folks with whom we love to spend our time, for we are always the better person in the presence of their blessing, wisdom, and depth.

When broken open by pain and loss, these broken open hearts become more capacious—roomy, comfortable, large, spacious, with an expanded capacity for grace, acceptance, and love of the other. You know these folks as well, and love to spend time with them. We love their "energy."

Back in the summer of 1989 my business partner Jerry and his son, 13-year-old Ryan, died in a car accident. Half of Karen's family was gone in an instant. Gone forever. Never coming back. Yet her heart remained soft and open. What a wonder and mystery to behold. A few decades after the gruesome tragedy, she describes her life with her former husband and son as a "sweet memory." I suspect it was surrender that some way, somehow helped Karen not only survive an unimaginable loss but build a second life of joy.

Living into what has become a heartbroken way of life for a decade or so now, sometimes well and at times poorly, has yielded an awareness that caught me by surprise. I'm happy. Maybe joyful is more accurate. Not all the time, of course. But, even without a soul mate, though missing the reassurance of one who believes in me, when the house is empty and cold, bereft of the countless discussions about everyday life, absent of warmth in the dark of the night, no one asking what I'd like for dinner or how far I rode my bike today, nobody saying I look good in that shirt, while eating alone, or even without that strangely comforting insightful critique that used to come my way—I still am joyful a good bit of the time. It is a deeper, more spiritual, primitive joy than before, when all seemed on track and the trajectory of life supported my happiness, whatever that word means.

Parker Palmer's view on the broken heart, whether broken apart or open, gives a clue as to how this might be possible for me—a deep joy in the face of penetrating loss. I spent far too many years resisting reality. I kept telling myself Janene will not and cannot possibly be losing her amazing mind in spite of the growing evidence to the contrary. All that energy spent on opposing, counteracting, holding the line, rebuffing, combating, driving back, contesting, denying, defending, and attempting to stem the tide of a progressive neurological disorder for which there is no remedy. It wore me out. And my heart... it was getting harder and smaller.

Maria Popova, in her brilliant "Brain Pickings" blog quotes Elizabeth Gilbert in her reflections on loss and grief. Consider this.

> I have learned that Grief is a force of energy that cannot be controlled or predicted. It comes and goes on its own schedule. Grief does not obey your plans or your wishes. It comes when it wants to. It's this tremendously forceful arrival and it cannot be resisted without you suffering more...and when it

is done, it will leave. But to stiffen, to resist, and to fight is to hurt yourself. The posture you take is you hit your knees in absolute humility and you let it rock you until it is done.

Grief says, "She's gone and she's never coming back."

I reply, "I am willing for that to be true."

Grief says, "You will never love like that again."

I reply, "I am willing for that to be true."

Grief says, "You will never hear that laugh again."

I say, "I am willing."

Grief says, "You will never smell her skin again."

I get down on the floor on my fucking knees, and—through sheets of tears—I say, "I AM WILLING."

This is the job of living—to be willing to bow down before EVERYTHING that is bigger than you. And nearly everything is bigger than you.[3]

There it is—raw, unvarnished surrender. I am now certain surrender is the only way to redeem my broken heart. Paradoxical and counterintuitive as it may be—and oh how it goes against my grain—only by humbly embracing this unwelcome grief will my heart break open and feed the souls of those in my circles of influence.

Popova puts it this way:

...out of the burning embers of loss arises an ashen

humility, true to its shared Latin root with the word humus. We are made 'of the earth' and we bow down low, we become crust…it is only when we give ourselves over to it completely that we can begin to take ourselves back, to rise, to live again.[4]

Ashen humility that gives rise to new life. That quality is in dramatically short supply these days. This notion of grief-incubated humility is what, much to our surprise, liturgical Christianity in its archaic forms reminds us of every Ash Wednesday.

"Remember that you are dust, and to dust you shall return" is the language of the priest when placing the ashes on the parishioner's forehead.

Perhaps this humble surrender is one of those archetypal processes on the road to joy. Take an obvious one—love. When this University of Iowa farm boy met a beautiful Longhorn co-ed from suburban Dallas, I didn't orchestrate, manage, or architect what would happen next and how. I gave myself over to the possibilities of love and companionship. I didn't control each heart-throbbing step of the adventure. Love has its own agenda, its own timing. And, I was blessed with many rich years of joy with Janene for letting love flow. It seems to be the same with grief.

So now, our life together is ending, heartbreakingly so. Her eyes will never sparkle like they once did. Am I willing for that to be true? Will I embrace each declining stage of the disease? Will I believe an ashen humility serves me well for the unfamiliar territory ahead? Am I able to bow before this arrival that is bigger than I? Can I be an openhearted husband to Janene in this last season of her life? And will I surrender to this grief and loss that has become mine?

In September of 1989 I found myself standing on the bank of the Yampa River as it meanders lazily through Steamboat Springs trying as best I could to accept, process, and yes, surrender to the enormity of the loss of my business partner and best friend, Jerry. Through the blurry vision of my tears I noticed a stack of wood deposited on the bank nearby during the high water of the customary spring runoff. I picked up a stick, threw it as far upstream as I could, and watched intently as it passed by and made its way down the Yampa, around the bend and out of sight. And then I repeated the ritual again. And again. And again. Each stick represented some dimension of the camaraderie and plans that would not be fulfilled and that I was offering up, surrendering to the flow of the river, and of my life without Jerry.

Nature and ritual have been a consistent resource to me over the last 30 plus years in the face of loss. The Yampa, headwaters of the Arkansas, the South Platte, and the North Platte rivers have all contributed to a healthy concession and nonresistance. I am grateful for them and their Creator. They help me surrender to the inevitability of departures as the decades accrue. Mom, Dad, Jim, Jerry, Dick, and now Janene's long goodbye. Loss always has a name.

22 | RADICAL HOPE

In the spring of 1973 Janene and I were introduced to the devastating effects of false hope. She was in tip-top physical condition, six months pregnant, and increasingly certain that something had gone drastically wrong with the baby. Everyone, especially our close friends, were sure she was wrong and reassured us everything would be fine. We were young, healthy, and faithful, so there was no reason to see the proverbial cup as half empty.

Determined to get to the truth of the matter as Janene was want to do, she decided to put the simple 1970s fetal monitor on herself at the end of a night shift in the labor and delivery department of St. Luke's hospital in Houston where she was working as a new RN. And as it turned out, Janene was right. There was no heartbeat. She arrived home at midnight devastated. It was a long and sleepless night.

Amongst the ways we human beings prepare for the possibility of suffering, especially protracted, interminable pain like dementia, is to rely on what psychology calls "magical thinking," the belief that one's own thoughts will consistently influence the external world and our desired outcomes. This is not to say that the practice of "the power of positive thinking" is always unhelpful, or that the schools of behavioral and cognitive psychology have not given us a model to reframe our negative, sometimes self-incriminating beliefs. We all know where we end up when unable to stop fearful, dread-filled thoughts from swirling and recycling and ricocheting through our minds. But too often even self-help tools can be a sophisticated form of false hopes. Then too, perhaps there are times when the new reality being thrust upon us is simply too big to absorb at once, and false hopes can give us a bit of time to catch our emotional breath.

And at the time of this writing, most of America is struggling to make just that sort of adjustment in the fourth week of a "lock down," a "sheltering-in-place" mandate in an attempt to slow the devastation of COVID-19 that has brought the entire world to its knees. We witnessed an early false hope announcement in the face of the oncoming pandemic from Washington assuring us we would all be in our church pews together by Easter Sunday morning, assuming that's where we wanted to be. That was yesterday. On the pinnacle Sunday of the Christian calendar, churches across America and around the world stood empty.

In an understandable attempt to reassure a country that COVID would be a short-lived blizzard and not the beginning of winter, we were given the false hope that things would return to some form of normalcy in just a few short weeks. It may be COVID, or the message from a fetal-monitor, the phone call forever riveted in your memory, the look on the doctor's face, the decision to end life support, a final no from the bank or investor, the "it's over" conversation with the once love of your life. All of us will be brought face-to-face with the reality that life, as we have known it, is ending, and the future is requiring something more from us.

What is needed when the best of emotional, psychological, or spiritual efforts and answers fall short as a tsunami of disruption is bearing down on us is what University of Chicago philosophy professor, Jonathan Lear, calls radical hope. In his book by that title, *Radical Hope: Ethics in the Face of Cultural Devastation*, Lear makes a careful study of Plenty Coups (1848-1932), the last great chief of the Crow nation in Montana, who represents this nuanced form of hope.

In the losing clash of cultures, the war for the American West, and after his people were sequestered on the reservation, Plenty Coups told author Frank B. Linderman that "when the buffalo went away the hearts of my people fell to the ground, and they could not lift them up again. After this nothing happened."[1]

In the face of cultural deconstruction, Lear reports that this Native American chief became a successful farmer, headed a Crow delegation to Washington, DC, visited Mt. Vernon, negotiated with the Catholic missionaries to found a school, donated his own home to the nation, and lived a productive life through the collapse of his civilization. In the face of a cultural upheaval Plenty Coups continued to lead his people.

What made the Crow leader's hope radical, Lear goes on to say, is "that it is directed toward a future goodness that transcends the current ability to understand what it is. Radical hope anticipates a good for which those who have the hope as yet lack the concepts with which to understand it."

Let me put a finer personal point on these lofty thoughts, with my first, false hope by way of contrast. I was sure Janene would be able to stay in our home indefinitely with in-home care after her diagnosis. With careful research I could surely find an inexpensive memory care facility if her decline eventually required it. My friends, family, and faith community would all be able to go the distance with her. And most of all, this would not last longer than a decade.

None of those hopes materialized, of course. Like the certitude that so-called Christian America will be back in church Easter Sunday of 2020, I had architected, orchestrated, and imagined specifically what the future was going to look like and was hanging onto that framework for dear life... understandable and unhelpful "when our hearts fall to the ground."

That is exactly what Plenty Coups avoided. Instead he entrusted himself to a future that at the moment was unknown, unclear, and uncharted. His traditional forms of living the good life were destroyed. Yet he had held the belief that new forms of human flourishing would eventually emerge for himself and the Crow people.

Living with the crushing weight of current reality *and* living with a healthy hope for the future has been an enormous challenge for me on this pilgrimage with Janene. Hope, and certainly false hope, actually worked against me far too often. This is what Dasha Kiper so eloquently and brilliantly describes in her *American Scholar* article (September 7, 2015) entitled, "Hope is the Enemy." A psychologist and trainer of ALZ support group facilitators in New York City, Kiper nuances how intermittent lucidity with ALZ and dementia, or I would add remission in the course of cancer, can seduce a caregiver into thinking maybe, just *maybe* "dementia is just a phase."[2] With extraordinary empathy and understanding, Kiper elucidates the struggle to "abandon hope" and embrace reality as best we can.

Even with 15 years of practice adjusting to the steady march of FTD on Janene's personality and identity under my belt, there are times I still can't lift my heart off the ground much like my fellow Native American friends of times past. Grief will arrive whenever it chooses.

I've learned that false hope is indeed the enemy. I've come to believe that J.R.R. Tolkien said it well that "false hopes are more dangerous than fears."[3] False hopes seem to always keep me one step away from dealing with things as they are.

When Abraham heard The Voice say to leave his homeland in Ur of the Chaldeans for some faraway promised land as the Hebrew story goes, he must have accessed a radical hope in his soul. It is said of him that he "obeyed and went, even though he did not know where he was going."[4] He must have managed the anxiety of not knowing well enough to respond.

Victor Frankl, the author of *Man's Search for Meaning* and survivor of the concentration camp misery observed that the ones who died at the hands of the Nazis clung to the false hope that freedom, return to their intact families, and the certainty of their imagined future would somehow make the suffering worthwhile. They were unable to live meaningfully into their current suffering *and* grasp a strong, though uncertain, hope for the future. It cost many of them their lives.[5]

C. S. Lewis, the prolific British author, once said, "It is only a matter of *when* not *if* we will concede."[6] He went on to say that the real question is *how* we will concede, gracefully or not? Plenty Coups conceded to cultural devastation, Frankl to the Nazis, and Lewis to cancer, which claimed his wife after four short years of happy marriage. But each did so with great courage, grace, and a radical hope for the future. And along with a host of others, they left a legacy for us to emulate.

You and I, we each face our own unique and particular calamity and collapse, if not now, a little later. COVID-19 reminds us of that truth. We are dramatically more vulnerable as individuals, as a society, or a global family, than we want to admit to our resilient and autonomous selves. So may we together find within ourselves, our communities, and in our spiritual roots a radical hope that helps us stay the course in these challenging and turbulent times.

23 | SWEET LAMENT

With the stealth and quiet of the mountain lion found here in the Colorado Rockies, FTD crept slowly into my marriage and stole the essence of my soul mate. That was the first encroachment. Then another unseen intruder—COVID-19—invaded, along with the rest of the world, my personal life. And last week, I found myself at 2000 South Blackhawk Street outside the C-3 room window of the quarantined New Dawn Memory Care, waving at my dear Janene, who is now sequestered without visitors, hoping that her demented mind would still be able to patch together some semblance of the love we once expressed with all our hearts, minds, and bodies. The necessary institutional lockdown for our most vulnerable in the face of this unmerciful virus is adding absurd insult to my already insufferable injury. The few dangling threads of remaining connection with Janene like touch, face-to-face contact, and essential presence are now cut.

So to accuse COVID of "Adding insult to injury" and "Pouring salt in your wound," the oft-used phrases for making a bad situation worse, seems fitting. It's really an unhelpful, mostly powerless response to yet another life circumstance over which I and we have no control. But sometimes indulging in self-pity and victimization seems to offer a short-lived relief. Sometimes.

After this so-called "window visit" with Janene, something caught me by complete surprise. I felt some sort of sweetness about the experience. Perhaps it was the kind inflection in her voice when she saw me. Or maybe it was the tenderness in her eyes. Or it might have been when she pressed her hand against the window and I almost "lost it." But while Janene's response of sweetness through the mediated window touched me, what I suspect may actually be emerging within me over this now 15-year FTD pilgrimage with Janene is a matter of the soul. A sweet lament is what my cropped encounter with Janene occasioned.

"Sweet lament" is a term my well-informed friend Dan Russ introduced me to a few years ago with his spiritual depth and PhD in Literature and Psychology. Though the term has fallen out of common usage in the West, we still find it in literary expression and in the sacred texts of the Jewish religion. Dan reminded me of a passage in Toni Morrison's *The Bluest Eye*, where Claudia is living with an angry, bitter mother in a racist culture but finds that when her mother was in a singing mood it wasn't so bad.

She would sing about hard times, bad times, and somebody-done-gone-and-left-me times. But her voice was so sweet and her singing eyes so melty I found myself longing for those hard times…Misery colored by the greens and blues of my mother's voice took all of the grief out of the words and left me with a conviction that pain was not only endurable, it was sweet.[1]

Dan's interpretation of this account was equally unexpected. "Claudia's experience is not an escape from reality, but a transformed reality. Her mother's blues transformed that ramshackle house from a prison that Claudia wanted to escape from into a sanctuary of sweet lament."

Since my New Dawn window visit, I've followed my curiosity about this notion of lament. I'll share a few of my findings in the hopes that "lament" may find its way back into your vocabulary as it has mine when facing the unresolvable.

Anglican author and scholar, N. T. Wright writes that lament is what happens when people ask "Why?" and don't get an answer. He recognizes our educated and scientific need for everything to have an explanation, but supposing it doesn't. Maybe real human wisdom, Wright suggests, doesn't mean being able to string together our speculations or explanations so we get a big sigh of relief. He believes that perhaps what we need most is to recover the biblical tradition of lament.[2]

In the 15-plus years I've had to observe my own and other's

anxious, hasty rush to make sense out of Janene's illness, and COVID-19 of late, it seems we humans, and especially we Americans, have an enormously difficult time looking unresolved pain, meaninglessness, or purposelessness in the eye. So I found comfort in the thoughts of Ryan Tafilowski, Denver Seminary professor and Edinburgh PhD, when he notes that, "For the biblical writers, the feeling of helplessness in the face of open-ended, unintelligible pain was a simple fact of life in a fallen world, and lament was one expression of an emotionally sophisticated and realistic spirituality, as much as joy or wonder or gratitude or longing."[3]

I'm no biblical scholar, but I suspect the individuals the writers referred to here are folks like the prophet Jeremiah who devotes a whole book of poetry to the desperate, but not hopeless, plight of the Hebrew nation in captivity. His book entitled simply "Lamentations," assumes the Jewish God is personal and one with whom we can contend in the midst of suffering and doom with the whole range of our emotions—rage, anger, accusation, disappointment, grief, jealousy, blame, doubt, and, paradoxically, hope. Here is how this piece of wisdom literature expresses what we might call a non-dualistic approach, both/and thinking, or perhaps holding the tension between darkness and light as we engage the inexplicable.

I remember my affliction and my wandering,
the bitterness and the gall.
I well remember them,

and my soul is downcast within me.
Yet this I call to mind,
and therefore I have hope.
Because of the Lord's great love we are not consumed,
for his compassions never fail.
They are new every morning,
great is your faithfulness.[4]

Then I recalled some ten-plus years ago Janene and I sang in the Spirituals Choir founded by Denver University psychology professor, Art Jones, and my childhood friend, Arlen Hershberger, with his degree in music from the University of Iowa. Janene had a rich alto voice. And I was further reminded that the most influential use of the lament tradition in America is, of course, the African-American spiritual. As we know so well, this genre of music, born out of slavery's shameful horrors, gives expression to both the immediacy of suffering and the freedom transcendence offers. What a sweet memory it is, perhaps a sweet lament as well, to recall the Thursday evenings when Janene and I joined our voices in the lyrics of that well-known spiritual.

Nobody knows the trouble I've seen
Nobody knows my sorrows
Nobody knows the trouble I've seen
Glory, hallelujah.

Sometimes I'm up sometimes I'm down
Oh, yes, Lord
Sometimes I'm almost to the ground
Oh, yes, Lord.

If you get there before I do
Oh, yes, Lord
Tell all my friends I'm comin' too
Oh, yes, Lord.

Oh, nobody knows the trouble I see
Nobody knows but Jesus
Nobody knows the trouble I see
Glory, hallelujah.[5]

Do give yourself permission to lament. Contend with the Universe, God, and Fate, or Life. I trust you will find, on occasion, even a sweet lament in your spiritual tradition as I have in mine in the words of this familiar spiritual. And just maybe, like for Claudia, it will help us transform our challenging reality.

24 | INCARNATION OR SCAR TISSUE

Amongst the insidious and seductive effects of early onset dementia in a loved one is the deconstruction of a shared life narrative and sense of purpose. What were heretofore decades of meaningful and intimate conversation with Janene about love, marriage, children, parenting, career, families of origin, money, predestination, suffering, politics, calling, and a plethora of other topics her extraordinary intellectual curiosity would light upon and I so thoroughly enjoyed, are replaced with pedestrian talk of the lunch menu, or no conversation at all much of the time, as the left brain loses its semantic capacity.

And in spite of the modest contribution of psychological understanding embedded in terms like enmeshment and codependency, we are still social beings, made to find meaning in the daily life of intimacy and autonomy. So when the very substance of a good enough marriage—soul mate communication—dries up and withers away, it is an enormously difficult adjustment. At least it was for me, and I have been struggling to navigate my way through this foreign, and for the most part, existentially challenging territory.

Not only are these interpersonal challenges, they are spiritual and philosophical matters as well. In the face of a dismantled past and no prospect of the future Janene and I had so frequently talked about, the questions of meaning eventually tracked me down. And in the dark of the night, when despair sometimes knocks at the door, I can wonder if Sartre and Nietzsche, the notorious existentialists were right that all we have is the present moment and any thinking person knows that God is dead. When the emotional chips are down and God, whatever our image of him or her might be, is deafeningly silent, what starts as a small mountain stream of negative rumination in my mind can cascade down the mountainside of my psyche into a whitewater river of self-doubt, meaninglessness, and hopelessness. The 3:00 a.m. darkness only adds to the descent.

And then these spiritual and philosophic struggles and complexities quickly leave the conceptual arena and become intensely practical in the redesigned warp and woof of everyday life. What about all the hundreds of hours I spent with Janene fruitlessly discussing her professional career before her diagnosis? What of the thousands upon thousands of dollars spent on the best therapists in Denver all to no avail because FTD makes both insight oriented and behavioral approaches ineffective? Since she no longer remembers our shared life as a couple or a family, how do I understand the meaning of all that personal history without a companion? And then the enormous investment we both made in the nurture and development of our marriage… and to have it end like this? And how do I find a way to live a meaningful fourth quarter of life when all Janene and I had hoped for, dreamed of, and had countless hours of conversation about our retirement years is now forever gone? How do I keep from resenting not only the loss of Janene's extraordinary earning capacity we were about to realize, but also the enormous expense of her memory care facility? In the face of this fundamental deconstruction of life as I thought it would be, how do I find meaning and purpose in both the past and look to the future with some reconstructed sense of fulfillment?

Well, I am certainly not the first to stare down the barrel of a Plan B thrust upon humanity through sickness, financial ruin, accident, divorce, bad decisions, or tragedy in all of its recalcitrant and perverse forms. Many have found hope and lived remarkably successful and redemptive lives in the face of deep reaching loss. They have found the hidden gem in the midst of their suffering. They have found the counterintuitive truth about being a "loser" as Novelist Pat Conroy puts it in his memoir, *My Losing Season*: "…winning makes you think you will always get the girl, land the job, deposit the million-dollar check, win the promotion, and you grow accustomed to a life of answered prayer. Loss is a fiercer, more uncompromising teacher, coldhearted but clear-eyed that life is more dilemma than game, and more trial than free pass…there is no teacher more discriminating and transforming than loss."[1]

The truth is, that far too many others have never recovered. They have "never been the same" since they were required to live a life that they worked tenaciously for decades to avoid. And in the case of the caretakers of dementia and Alzheimer's, their rate of death and illness is much higher than the national norms for obvious reasons. Dementia has its own unique set of challenges for the family and friends…watching your loved one die "one word at a time;" living with "half a person" for years; having friends disappear because it is so socially awkward; the impossibility of starting over; the long goodbye, or never able to say goodbye; protracted, often uninsured medical costs; family disagreements over caretaker approaches, and so on. Like a heartland friend of mine once said, "Being the caretaker for a loved one with dementia is like a barn door withstanding the relentless wind of western Kansas; it eventually finds the weak bolt or screw and works it loose."

Conroy goes on to describe when he resurrected and re-connected his losing season basketball team of '67 at The Citadel in order to write the memoir, that he "found instead of memory there was scar tissue and nerve damage" some 30 years later. That is what I hope and pray will not be said of me years from now, that I had not healed and my range of motion in life was limited by my experience of losing my best friend and marriage companion to the early onset of an incurable and mean-spirited disease.

On the morning of December 12, 1992, in southeastern Iowa at the memorial service for my mother's untimely death, I heard my father's response to an ill-advised question from one of his friends.

"What are you going to do now, Clark?"

To which Dad responded, "What kind of question is that? I am going to make it through this and move on with my life!"

There was no scar tissue in Dad' response. No bitterness or regret or despondency, or powerlessness about the next season of life without Mom. No "nerve damage" in this uneducated but wise Iowa farmer. In fact, I learned from several of dad's friends on my infrequent visits home after he passed away, that when these men and women lost their spouses, dad wrote them a letter on how to find meaning in life without their lifelong companion. At the ripe old age of 85, my father somehow transformed an often life crippling loss that prematurely ends the life of a longtime husband of wife, into a redemptive outreach for others in his tiny circle of influence in a tiny southeastern Iowa hamlet until his own passing at almost 91.

There's an arcane and mostly unheard-of element in Judeo-Christian thought called "incarnational theology" that might shed a bit of light on Dad's last six years of life. It's this notion that a person, a human being, can actually embody a spiritual reality like mercy, forgiveness, grace, and of course, love. That our body, and an activity in which we are engaged with another, can convey an essentially spiritual message and our person is only the channel through which a deeper truth is being conveyed.

Teilhard de Chardin, the Jesuit French philosopher captured this notion in one dense and thought-provoking sentence… "We are not human beings having a spiritual experience; we are spiritual beings having a human experience."[2]

It's an enormous challenge to not let "scar tissue and nerve damage" develop in our soul during seasons of loss, suffering in all its forms, tragedy, and pain. They can all be discriminating and transforming teachers, as Conroy so keenly reminds us. That is, if we are willing to be students of life and embrace the life-long process of becoming spiritual beings in the face of the unavoidably common human experience of loss.

25 | FOR THE LONG HAUL

I USED TO ENJOY hearing and using the word "progressing." I was *progressing* toward the completion of my graduate degree back in the day. The new house that Janene and I dreamed of was under construction and *progressing* toward a March 1985 finish date. All three of our young daughters were *progressing* nicely through all their developmental benchmarks as children. Janene and I were *progressing* in our understanding of how to be married well.

This is how we normally think of this notion of "progressing"—it means advancement or development toward better or more complete conditions, improvement, moving forward, betterment, making headway, growth, to gain ground, make strides, and even flourish or blossom.

But when Dr. Ragsdale, the insightful and compassionate physician who attends to my wife's care in her ongoing battle with dementia, uses the word "progressing," none of the usual meanings apply. What progressing has come to mean in this part of my life is that Janene has lost yet another of the multitudinous functions that either her brain's frontal lobe or her temporal lobe once performed with precision and accuracy.

For instance, last week the doctor described her recent shuffling gate, her declined interest in escaping the secure facility, and her disinterest in healthy food in the now expected line: "Janene is progressing."

Amongst the many pernicious influences of dementia is how it completely rearranges the meaning of commonly used words or phrases. "Progress" will forever be redefined in my vocabulary. So will "I lost my mind," or its companion phrase we often use in a confusing situation or in the midst of an unsettling conundrum, "I must be losing my mind." "I had a senior moment" is no joking matter for me either. "We may have to lock you up," we sometimes quip with our friends when they are overly enthused or a bit tipsy. Those are some painful words to hear if your best friend and lifelong companion is confined to a locked, secure facility for the rest of her life.

We also have come to use common phrases to express matters of short or lengthy duration.

"It's just around the corner."

"In the short run."

"Don't hold your breath."

And perhaps the most common expression for the need of

preparation, right perspective, and resiliency in the face of a lengthy challenge: "We are in this for the long haul."

No matter how cliché these expressions may be, they all have an element of truth in them and they take on a whole different meaning if they give voice to our current reality.

So when what I had so tenaciously hoped, and sometimes fervently prayed, would be a short-term challenge evolved into a long-term, chronic, protracted, and seemingly interminable way of life with no end in sight, I then cast about for additional resources. The common place tips and tools from my well-intended friends and even many professionals quickly came up short in the face of what now is a multifaceted, emotional, social, spiritual, and financial conundrum that some of the best minds have attempted to address over the years.

Call it whatever you like: Plan B, the perfect storm, bad luck, suffering, bad karma, evil, or an act of God... these unwanted life circumstances that scoff at quick fixes, one-dimensional advise, and spiritual triumphalism, eventually will send us back to the drawing board in search of a resiliency that will sustain us through the uncharted territory.

At least that is what happened to me when my wife was diagnosed with FTD. Now what? To whom do I turn? What will give me staying power? As author Anne Lamott so poignantly writes in her book *Plan B: Further Thoughts on Faith*, sometimes our only prayer, and it certainly was the case for me, is a single word: "Help!"[1]

And the resources are often in short supply to build this

capacity to survive and yes, even flourish, when things go awry and stay awry, especially when progressing persists in the wrong direction.

If you were raised in a religious and spiritual environment as I certainly was, we naturally turn to our church, pastor, priest, or small group for the support we need. But sometimes even our faith community comes up short when the struggle is not easily remedied.

Over the years I have heard far too many stories of the aunt healed of cancer in Wichita or how after years of addiction "I now am set free," and too few authentic, vulnerable stories of folks in the midst of a mind and soul bending challenge asking for support or prayer. I am not saying these testimonies of divine intervention are inauthentic or sensationalistic, though they sometimes can be. But where are the people of faith who will walk the long and unpredictable road of dementia with me, and the many others for whom there are no answers and no victories or breakthroughs to report? Even faith communities are not immune to our cultural allergy to vulnerability and powerlessness. There are some life circumstances that simply will not yield to the normal spiritual resources we have at our disposal and have served us well under earlier circumstances.

If you happen to share my experience from earliest memories of having a relationship with who I believed to be a loving and companionable God, then the experience of God going dark or silent is disorienting. And sometimes surprisingly, I find that even my agnostic and skeptical friends still expect God to show up in the midst of personal calamity and profound loss. Yes, even God may not come through as the resource we hoped for during the long-haul challenge.

Maybe we can safely assume that the super-religious and Nobel Prize winning folks like Mother Teresa didn't have these dark nights of the soul. It turns out not to be the case. Since her death in 1997 and her sainthood in 2003, her longtime friend Brian Kolodiejchuk authored a book, *Mother Teresa, Come Be My Light: The Private Writings of the Saint of Calcutta*, in which the previously unpublished personal journal of this astonishing servant of the poorest of the poor describes the silence of God that even she knew. Here is an example.

> The place of God in my soul is blank—There is no God in me—when the pain of longing is so great—I just long and long for God—and then it is that I feel—He does not want me—He is not there—Sometimes—I just hear my own heart cry out—'My God' and nothing else comes—The torture and pain I can't explain.[2]

There is a modicum of comfort knowing that this scarcity of spiritual resource I and we sometimes experience is not an isolated and new phenomenon. In spite of a fleeting ridiculous thought that I might well be the first to have gone through this fire, there are those, even the likes of the iconic Mother

Teresa who befriended the darkness, maintained a strong faith, and lived remarkably productive and inspiring lives.

Which brings me to an oft forgotten long haul resource—the superlative example of our ancestors. In an age where the contemporary is idolized and history is blithely dismissed as irrelevant in the face of 21st century complexity, we too often fail to recognize the strengths to be found in our family history or lineage. Granted, far too many families have left nothing but a painful and abusive legacy to their children whose lives are often in ruins and their spirits crushed. But even in what we have come to call "deeply dysfunctional" families, I have discovered that if one goes back far enough, there are people of character to be found who can give us an unsuspecting strength and courage for our current challenging reality.

This became powerfully and spiritually evident to me not but several months ago while visiting the Castle of Thun in Switzerland where eight generations ago in my family history, Melchior Brenneman was imprisoned for his Anabaptist faith. You may not be aware of this thin slice of church history in which my ancestors, known as the "Anabaptists" (because they opposed infant baptism) were persecuted and many martyred for this belief by the then unified church and state authorities.

Standing in the impeccably preserved fourth floor turret prison cell in which my ancestor suffered for his faith brought it home to me. Embedded in my family lineage are people of extraordinary character whose lives were radically changed and who met their own challenges with extraordinary courage.

Melchior, his wife, and seven children were exiled by the provincial rulers of the time to Germany, never to return to his Swiss homeland. This man's virtues are a part of my identity, in my DNA as we say, and I want them not to lie dormant or unclaimed now that I am so in need of them for the particular long-haul challenge that is mine.

A 1930s historian wrote this of my ancestor and how those of us who follow might well be inspired.

> The sacrifices that Melchoir and his wife made for the ideal of religious liberty should not be lightly passed over by us, their descendants. Their lives should stand out before us on the page of history as lives of purest heroism. They should be an ever-living inspiration to their thousands upon thousands of descendants...[3]

Author David Whyte puts it so well in his *Crossing the Unknown Sea: Work as a Pilgrimage of Identity.*

> Each of us has some kind of tenacious family ancestry to call on... somewhere in each of our backgrounds lies a layered, gritty complexity, an inheritance of people who came through.[4]

Sankofa is a word from Ghana that translates "Go back and get it." There is a Denver-based choir by the name of Sankofa that performs what I grew up calling Negro Spirituals, whose mission is to recover the meaning and inspiration of that ancestral genre of music born out of a painfully dark time in our country's history. Sometimes it may be just that simple.

Maybe we need to humble ourselves in order to go back and get the stories and narrative of our ancestors, who lived in dramatically different times, of course, but in their own often uneducated way, who modeled for us virtues that are timeless and would serve us well in the face of present-day obstacles.

I recently came across one of Maria Popova's well-honed thoughts on her "Brain Pickings" blog that summed up well the challenge of a protracted challenge.

> In every life, there comes a time when we are razed
> to the bone of our resilience by losses beyond our
> control—lacerations of the heart that feel barely
> bearable, that leave us bereft of solid ground.
> What then?[5]

An unsuspecting bit of solid ground for my own prolonged heartbrokenness came from a deepened appreciation of the inheritance provided by those of my ancestors who found a way through. They were and are an ever-living inspiration to me. And there may well be those folks in your lineage too, who are exemplars of courage and grit for your own long haul, incalcitrant challenge. And to take a bit of anthropomorphic license, I suspect those who have gone on before are smiling to know we are standing in the stream of their exceptional faith and courage.

So, yes, support for the long haul can come from unsuspected sources. I can't really blame a faith community for struggling to keep up with the arduous grind of providing support to a relentlessly afflicted friend, and even God's silence can be a way of directing our weary souls to an unexpected place of comfort. I was simply checking Switzerland off my bucket list, and here I was, standing in a castle turret prison, receiving support, inspiration, strength from family members long gone. O divine mysterium.

26 | RANCH ROAD 1222

ROAD BIKING TEXAS Ranch Road 1222 during the height of the bluebonnet season has long been on my bucket list. This 15-mile stretch of blacktop winds its way between Mason and Brady in the very heart of the Texas Hill Country. Live oaks shade it in the morning and evening hours. Rich folk from Dallas and Austin have not "spoilt," as they say here, the quaint, four to five generation ranch homes and pastoral terrain of rolling hills. With spring rains, like this year supplied, the bluebonnets and Indian paintbrush along the roadside erupt into a virtual blanket of indigo for mile after breathtaking mile. And, there is ample roadkill of the ill-fated possum, raccoon, snake, rabbit, turtle, and the iconic armadillo to keep even the veteran road biker from falling asleep at the wheel.

This morning my dream ride and reality converged. It was a perfect Hill Country morning. Cloudless skies. Westerly breeze. 71 degrees. Goats grazing. Humid. Abundant blue-bonnets. Curious Longhorns. One-finger rancher waves. My Specialized Roubaix and I were one, as we like to say in the biking world. It was a near perfect convergence of non-essential, material dreams and an actual experience. Even my high-flying expectations were exceeded. Life was great. These are precious moments to be appreciated and experienced with a robust joy.

As great as this morning was, I found my mind drifting to another whole line of thinking. It went something like this.

How well do I respond when things don't turn out so perfectly?

I began thinking about being thrust into Plan B, where my life, and the life of those I love gets derailed by events well beyond our exaggerated sense of control and power. What if things don't work out? What if we are no longer talking about fun, trivial expectations like bike rides, but major life dreams that are shattered? Early dementia. Pancreatic cancer. Unwanted divorce. Sexual addiction. Infertility. Suicide. Unavoidable bankruptcy. Mental illness. A debilitating stroke. A bitter ex. Addicted children. Professional failures. To name but a few Plan B or even C disruptions. How do I respond when an enormous gap emerges between my expectations and my current reality of life? And how do I respond when I am missing out, and no amount of intellectual, spiritual, or professional effort will change the reality that I am now facing? What then? That's what I have been thinking about.

Here in Texas they describe a common and harsh weather pattern that changes the best-laid plan and intention as a "blue norther." It consists of strong northerly winds, rain, sleet, high humidity, and sometimes snow. These storms are miserable, and they tend to disrupt even what we thought were the most important of plans. They often come quickly, without warning, and literally, will change the landscape of a predictable plan overnight, not unlike what so many of us have come to find true of our lives and our current reality.

These "blue northers" of life, as it were, almost without exception, rob us of the life that we thought we were going to live, or hoped we would be living. In spite of our protestations, they put Plan B solidly in place and require a response on our part, gracious or otherwise. What about the life that we had dreamed of and hoped we would now be living and are not? Is it worth examining?

Adam Phillips, in *Missing Out: In Praise of the Unlived Life* argues that our unlived lives define and transform us just like, and perhaps more so, than the lives we are actually living. Perhaps, even this unrealized life is what makes us who we are. The late country music legend Merle Haggard, not known for his philosophic reflection, believed that the early death of his father and all the subsequent trouble he got into because he grew up fatherless, contributed greatly to who he became and the body of music he birthed.[1]

In an age of rampant individualism and obsessive self-actualization it is not easy to quiet the internal voices that insist we are missing out, or that we are not living up to our potential. They build quite a compelling argument to justify our anger, resentment, blame of others, depression, disgust for God, self-pity, envy, and sense of entitlement, to name only a few of the emotional demons that sometimes torment us in the face of a widening gap between hopes and reality.

I am reminded of what my father said on the first anniversary of mom's death:

> "I wonder what there is for me to learn in all of this?"
>
> It is noteworthy that amongst the questions Dad didn't ask were: "Why did this happen to me?" "What is God trying to teach me?"
>
> Or... "What could I have done to keep your mother from driving that snowy day?"

For my father, Mom preceding him in death and living without her companionship after 57 years of marriage was undoubtedly the most painful and unimaginable of gaps between wishes and reality. And yet, his wisdom and faith enabled a posture of growth and transformation in the face of the unthinkable.

And I recall further what Dad said the first morning without Mom after a sleepless night where now the sun rose on an unwanted Plan B that had ambushed his life at the ripe age of 85.

"This is absolutely devastating, but your mother and I had 57 good years."

Amazing.

He was able to hold together, even in the initial shock of his unspeakable loss, both gratitude and grief. This capacity to hold opposites together, to see different aspects of the truth, is what we now call "polarity management," a focus of leadership and organizational development. It is the refusal to apply simplistic, one-dimensional solutions to life realities that create enormous philosophical and spiritual conundrums. Common examples of these one-sided approaches come from our modernistic friends who believe the Universe ordains all things and our fundamentalist Christian friends who, on the other hand, insist that even the cruelest of circumstances are "God's will and He is in control." Our souls know the lack of wisdom when we encounter intellectual gymnastics in the well-intended.

What Dad knew without ever cracking either a high school or college textbook was that grief and gratitude can and must co-exist if we are to make a reasonably good adjustment to Plan B.

There is much to be said for the affluent, educated life of choice and potential that many of us are privileged to live. It does offer more than a few possibilities and pathways of fulfillment to many. But what I don't want happening to me in the face of either trivial or life-changing disappointment is what Phillips describes: "the myth of potential can make of our lives a perpetual falling-short, a continual and continuing loss, a sustained and sustaining rage...making our mourning and complaining feel like the realest things we ever do; and makes our frustration a secret life of grudges."

I want to be counted among the many, my father included, who have the spiritual and emotional fortitude to explore the meanings and significance of their unlived lives and losses. And just maybe you and I will find in those unlived lives that we aren't really missing out, or more accurately, not in the way we often think.

Perhaps we will discover, if we can manage our disappointment and sense of entitlement well enough, that by embracing our unlived lives we can experience what Saint Paul asserts that "in all things God works for the good of those who love Him..."[2] Maybe the "blue northers" of life bring with them treasures of wisdom and character that the perfect mornings on Ranch Road 1222 simply cannot deliver.

27 | STOUTHEARTED

I AM SO TIRED of being stouthearted… bone-tired of it. "Bone-tired" was the term I grew up with as an Iowa farm boy and sometimes heard at the end of a harvest season or haying season when a sustained, prolonged, determined, persevering, continuous, and undaunted effort had been required. It went beyond muscle tiredness. That requires just a good night's sleep. Bone-tired was reserved to describe extreme exhaustion, deep fatigue, or an utter weariness with the potential to reach the soul, a depleting of spirit even in the face of a significant accomplishment.

It was Frontotemporal Dementia that asked of me a stout-heartedness for which I was totally unprepared. That was a staggering seventeen years ago as of this writing. How could I have possibly known what was in store and what was about to be required of me as my dear soul mate began her descent at the hands of an unyielding, merciless, and often cruel progressive neurological disorder? Along with the millions who care for a loved one with Alzheimer's Disease or who find themselves face-to-face with the impenetrable mystery of suffering, I have needed every one of the following lengthy list of stouthearted features over the last seventeen years—many times over—just to survive:

Bold

Heroic

Noble

Self-reliant

Manful

Audacious

Brave

Confident

Daring

Undaunted

Firm

Gallant

Hardy

Lion-hearted

Resolute

Staunch

Robust

Strong

Today, just reading the list is exhausting. And having a

courageous spirit seems nearly impossible. As one of the men in my Alzheimer's support group said recently, "This disease has beaten me down." The truth is that there are moments, days, and stretches of time in the face of unflinching, protracted pain and suffering when the admonition of Job's wife seems compelling: "Curse God and die."

It seems Job's wife was overreacting a bit. But then again, I, along with you fellow caregivers and co-sufferers, can say that it is no small challenge to watch a loved one suffer and decline for whatever reason. An overreaction or two seems forgivable.

An obscure and forgotten word that best describes what I battle within this never-ending struggle with dementia's capture of my wife is *acedia*—carelessness, apathy, listlessness, and melancholia. Kathleen Norris, the award-winning poet and author, interprets this ancient word and its contemporary application in her book *Acedia and Me*.

> I think it likely that much of the restless boredom, frantic escapism, commitment phobia, and ener-vating despair that plagues us today is the ancient demon of acedia in modern dress.
>
> The person afflicted by acedia refuses to care or is incapable of doing so. When life becomes too challenging and engagement with others too demanding, acedia offers a kind of spiritual mor-phine; you know the pain is there, yet can't rouse yourself to give a damn.[1]

I could use a shot of "spiritual morphine" today to number the stark reality that marked Janene's 71st birthday. With the legislated necessity of social distancing in the face of our current worldwide COVID-19 pandemic and the lockdown of all elder care facilities, I found myself bringing Janene a birthday cake and singing "Happy Birthday" through her room C-3 window at the memory care facility. She could neither comprehend it was her birthday nor recognize me. My visit lasted about 60 seconds until she turned away from the window and walked back into the dining hall. It was a very long minute.

Rousing a courageous, stouthearted spirit proves to be out of reach on this particular day. At the unceremonious ending to the visit I hastened to the car before bursting into tears. It was on birthdays that Janene's true affirming and life-giving essence had come to the fore. My and our daughter's favorite meals and desserts were, without exception, the entrée on our birthdays. She made certain that each of our girls and I felt special, welcome, and that we occupied a unique and unprecedented place in this world that was only ours to fill on what she came to call "our special day." And, she could internalize the affirmation and love she received from our daughters and me on her birthday as they entered adulthood and recognized her extraordinary gift to them.

But not this birthday as this celebratory person no longer knows what a birthday is nor how to celebrate it with those she loves.

Norris presents in her book how best to address the bone-tired, apathetic weariness that we sometimes simply cannot avoid when the unimaginable becomes reality, as it did for me today on Janene's "special day." Perhaps it will create a pathway back to a modicum of hope as it has for me from time to time.

> The boundaries between depression and acedia are notoriously fluid. At the risk of oversimplifying, I would suggest that while depression is an illness treatable by counseling and medication, acedia is a vice that is best countered by spiritual practices and the discipline of prayer.[2]

I think we sometimes make spiritual practices and disciplines a bit too esoteric and complicated. On occasion my spiritual practices include the ordinary stuff of life... a long walk without my phone, mowing the lawn, changing oil in my lawn mower, filling the bird feeder, a warm shower, planting the garden, a long bike ride, garden weeding, a journal entry, or even emptying the dishwasher.

If we breakdown the division between the sacred and the profane, a whole raft of possibilities emerge as "spiritual practices" loosely defined as that which feeds our soul.

It never ceases to amaze me when a simple trip to the garden yields a ripe tomato and also yields an emotional boost in an otherwise depressing and bone-tiring day. As good as they often are, the spiritual discipline needed on many of my acedia-filled days is not a weekend silent retreat or an hour of contemplative prayer. Just checking the early girl tomatoes will do.

28 | "TAKE A LARGER WAY"

IT BEGAN AS A normal visit. But what "normal" has come to mean when visiting my dear wife Janene who has fought this losing battle with dementia for nearly two decades is something like this… a childlike scream of delight upon seeing me, no meaningful verbal exchange, faraway looks of confusion, obsessive repetition of three short phrases, smiles in response to my touch, and impenetrable, mysterious, non-verbal messages from those enormous, steely blue eyes. It is strangely comforting and profoundly heartbreaking to be with her. Every time.

A normal visit also includes that tender moment that defies some of even the professional's pronouncements that "she really isn't there anymore," when Janene points to my wedding band, smiles, and puts her left hand on mine. And ever the hospitable hostess when I arrive for lunch, she tries with the precious few remaining words to direct the memory care staff to prepare my plate before hers. Never a bite will she take until I am situated to her satisfaction. So the gracious hostess element still remains however obscured by the onward march of her rare and pernicious disorder and gives testimony to her rich, Texas roots and traditions. Janene is not completely gone.

I find myself wanting to curate each word, each smile, each nuance of the person with whom I once lived a robust life, because it is likely she will soon be mute and may well not recognize me at all. Frontotemporal Dementia has long since stolen the lion's share of her vibrant personality stored in her frontal lobe. And her temporal lobe, custodian of the verbal and semantic function of who we are, has only three or four brief expressions that remain. So like the last day of an exhilarating vacation, or bite of the best steak ever, or seeing your youngest off to college, or savoring the remaining light of a glorious sunset, or whenever we know a mundane or life-changing necessary ending is upon us, we treasure the moment as the seemingly insignificant becomes sacred. These moments are transformed into works of art and treasures to honor and protect.

But I still was not prepared when a routine visit with Janene evolved into a spiritual awakening I may well be metabolizing for years to come. I was dumbfounded and stunned. Comforted too.

It began when I found her in the secure backyard sitting area basking in the Colorado sunshine whispering, "It's beautiful," one of her three remaining phrases. She was leaning back in one of those tattered, faded, begging to be replaced patio chairs, so I grabbed the other one and scooted it next to hers. Then with her eyes closed and nearly transfixed in the sunlight, while holding my hand she began to repeat these words and this phrase over and over in a soft, sweet, and inviting tone, "Take a larger way, take a larger way, take a larger way, take a larger way."

At first I anxiously shrugged it off as yet another nonsensical, meaningless communiqué that FTD is so adept at creating from even the most brilliant minds. She has lost the sequential, logical capacity to communicate meaning. Yet this puzzling sentence held together like none she had uttered in many months, maybe a year. And why repeat it? How could this verbiage have none of the urgent, almost torturous angst that so often accompanied Janene's failed attempts to put words to what was on her mind? Of all the millions of word combinations that she has lost, why would this unique arrangement of words be retained and express some desire of her heart?

So in a rare moment of Janene's contemplative mindfulness, I entered into this precious moment with her and listened as deeply as I could. And to my utter amazement, it became perfectly clear that Janene's spirit was sending a message to mine. Tears flooded down my face as I absorbed the intimacy of this most unexpected, unprecedented, and penetrating message.

What could it possibly mean?

And not only did I ponder the perplexing answer to how she could retrieve these words that have long since been gone, but why these exacting and particular words? I managed to contain my emotions well enough so as not to disturb Janene as she repeated this simple, profound phrase for at least three or four minutes with her eyes closed. Was it a prayer, a blessing, a ritual, a reassurance, a consecration, a Janene-like pep talk, an anointing, a liturgy, a calling, or a benediction?

I left the facility in a pondering frame of mind, yet certain of one thing—Janene had delivered a critically important message to me, unmistakably so.

Scarcely 24 hours had passed in my attempt to assimilate that sacred experience with Janene at New Dawn Memory Care, when I came upon yet another serendipitous confirmation of the message.

I am persevering with the bittersweet ritual of "going through her things," sorting her personal effects, reflecting on the abundance of journals and why she kept them, and marveling at the capacity of her mind to write and think about things that matter.

For instance, at the tender age of 14 from her home in Dallas, she wrote a page reflecting on the assassination of President Kennedy and that fateful day in November of '63. But most astonishing was a plaque given to Janene and me from a group of campus ministry staff I had managed in Texas, Oklahoma, and Arkansas when I left Houston for graduate studies at the University of Denver. It captured the lyrics to one of the walking songs penned by Bilbo Baggins, J.R.R. Tolkien's character in *The Hobbit*. Again, to my utter amazement, here are the words inscribed on the plaque which instantly brought yet another flood of confirming and appreciative tears.

The Road goes on and on
Down from the door where it began.
Now far ahead the Road has gone,
And I must follow, if I can,
Pursuing it with weary feet,
Until it joins some larger way,
Where many paths and errands meet.
And whither then? I cannot say.[1]

Amongst the inevitable and unavoidable consequences of dementia, or any progressive disease for that matter, is that life becomes small. The examples of this dreadful process in Janene's life are far too numerous to name, but just a few poignant ones: She once rode her bike two to three hours a day and now she eats three meals a day and walks 30 steps back to her room to rest. Her turbocharged mind once devoured nursing school anatomy and physiology texts and complained that nursing was too easy. Now she is unable to read. Attending a liturgical worship service was often a highlight of her week, but now she can't understand the word Eucharist, or know what the elements represent. And perhaps the most heartbreaking reduction of all, the three daughters into whose lives she poured her own for over 40 years she no longer recognizes. Pick whatever vantage point—physical, spiritual, social, intellectual, familial—Janene now lives in a shrunken world and existence that is unimaginably small.

So for my dear wife, from the depths of her truncated existence and in the unrelenting grip of a degenerative neurological disorder, to somehow mysteriously collaborate with none other than the likes of Tolkien on the notion that a larger way not only exists, but that I should take it—is mind-boggling, humbling, and perhaps more than anything else, profoundly encouraging.

Indeed, I am filled with wonder every time I recall the event, and even so as I now attempt to discern its meaning. A dear friend of mine captured the essence and spirit of her message by saying, "I believe what she is saying to you is from an extremely deep spiritual connection that is beyond our comprehension. We can only embrace it and gasp in absolute wonder."

I am not the only one to puzzle over what some larger way message from either a suffering spouse or a literary giant might mean. John Eldredge, author of *Sacred Romance* in reflecting on this passage from Tolkien puts it this way.

> The Sacred Romance calls to us every moment of our lives.
>
> It whispers to us on the wind, invites us through the laughter of good friends, reaches out to us through the touch of someone we love. We've heard it in our favorite music, sensed it at the birth of our first child, been drawn to it while watching

the shimmer of a sunset on the ocean. It is even present in times of great suffering—illness of a child, the loss of a marriage, the death of a friend. Something calls to us through experiences like these and rouses an inconsolable longing deep in our heart, wakening in us a yearning for intimacy, beauty, and adventure. This longing is the most powerful part of any human personality. It fuels our search for meaning, for wholeness, for a sense of being truly alive. However we may describe this deep desire, it is the most important thing about us, our heart of hearts, the passion of our life. And the voice that calls to us in this place is none other than the voice of God.[2]

Janene exuded this power of the human personality, the truly human larger way. She not only yearned for, but could deliver on the intimacy, beauty, and adventure to which Eldredge refers. She wrote a book on mid-life women's health and started a consulting business to meet the need, earned an MBA in her 50s, learned to ski in her 40s, road biked through the Rocky Mountains with Women on Wheels, chaired the board of Denver Inner City Health Center, went sky diving, served concurrently as both the CFO and COO of MOPS International, happily left her native Texas to support my graduate studies in Denver, and taught me volumes about intimacy in the first decades of our relationship. Before the

FTD era, Janene longed to be truly alive, to embrace the larger way, to be a soul mate, and to hear the voice of God in the midst of her fully engaged life.

And now, now that she is confined to this abridged small life, still she wants me to live a full, meaningful life.

In and through the Spirit, Janene must somehow know how tempting it is to take the smaller way, to allow this overpowering disease to define me and my life, to play small, or to turn my back on possibilities for the future.

Her message: "Don't let it happen. Take a larger way."

That is what took my breath away on the sun porch several Saturdays ago. It's a stunning thing to have not only a front row seat to tragedy and suffering, but also to know unconditional love of this depth and under these circumstances.

And to add another layer of meaning to Janene's already poignant message, she will occasionally add another word. It goes like this. "Take a larger *calling* away."

Only a few days ago, she somehow persuaded the staff to let her use a phone and called me leaving a two-minute message that repeated only these words with various inflections and emphases, "Take a larger calling away."

Janene wrestled with herself, her mind, her advisors, and God more than most about how to construct a fulfilling life. From early Bible-belt perspectives like "God has a wonderful plan for your life," to discerning the Lord's will, to discovering her unique abilities, to co-creating with the transcendent a life of meaning and purpose, Janene thought long and hard before using words like calling and vocation. She also had periods of existential doubt and skepticism, concluding that it must be God who was frustrating her vigorous attempts to find her own larger way. So it's not surprising actually, that she would add this powerful word "calling" to the message she so persistently wants me to hear.

We sometimes quip that "things happen in threes," for good or ill. Well, here is the third coincidence, random occurrence, or maybe divine synchronicity, depending on your point of view on the things that take us just beyond the reach of reason.

Within another 24 hours after Janene added the "calling" word to her message, I received the morning blog of Richard Rohr, the Franciscan, on the topic of vocation. Here's why it caught my attention and why my heart leapt again upon further reflection on the communiqué from Janene.

> Vocation is one way in which we discover our True Self. I'm not speaking so much about education, career, or livelihood...In general, it is a Larger Life that somehow calls us forward (vocation means a call or summons in Latin), more than we call it to us. You are a part of a larger thing called Life.
>
> You and I don't have to figure it all out, fix everything, or do life perfectly all by ourselves. All we have to do is participate in the One Life. To find our unique niche in that Always Larger Life is what we mean by vocation.[3]

"Summons." I love that word. It's so fitting here. And it puts an unsuspected twist to a traditional concept. In its simple form it means "an authoritative and urgent call for someone to be present or to do something." In the decades before the disease and when Janene was fully engaged as a wife, a mother, a sister, an executive, she never shied away from a summons—giving or receiving one. She expected no less from others than from herself… show up and deliver. Her message has remained the same.

When I reflect on the convergence of these three "coincidences," the power of these particular words in what may be Janene's last and loving summons to me, the experience with Janene's spirit on the sun porch, that in her diminished capacity she could still frame a clear, concise communiqué, I am reminded of two statements from Leif Enger's *Peace Like a River* when reporting on the inexplicable and mysterious.

> "Make of *that* what you will." *And…* "Listen: There are easier things than witnessing a miracle of God."[4]

29 | GRIEF AND GRATITUDE

SHORTLY AFTER THE agonizing task of sequestering Janene in the memory care facility against her will was completed, two women close to me made powerful statements to which I took great offense. The first came from my dementia coach and advisor whose husband was diagnosed with FTD twenty years prior, well before it was identified as one of the many ALZ cousins in the degenerative neurological world. She was no stranger to the plight of caregivers and loved ones. More than a few had profited from her decades of seasoned wisdom who like I were trying to metabolize the life-altering reality of The Disease.

"Remember, Janene has dementia; you don't" was her simple, frank message.

Really? Tell me something I don't know. How painfully obvious. A plethora of resistant emotions and thoughts flooded my mind.

But a decade later, what I know now is that my coach was watching me fall prey to a common occurrence—the decline of emotional, spiritual, and physical health in the committed caregiver.

Dementia is a powerfully seductive disease. It humbles the most gifted and sincere family members. It finds a weak seam in the fabric of an otherwise cohesive family. It brings judgment and ridicule into the lives of kind and caring loved ones. It causes people of faith to doubt the existence of God and certainly the goodness of God. It erodes life savings and destroys a secure financial future for many. And of course, many times it exhausts and depletes the body of the caregiver. It has no cure. It introduces many to their first encounter with depression and hopelessness. It is a mean disease. It can beat down the strongest with its unrelenting and unpredictable advance.

In spite of my hefty agrarian background, a good family of origin, strong faith, and circle of supportive friends, I was no exception to the universal rule that dementia comes after you and your family. It will draw you into its vortex and get you to think, do, and say what was heretofore unimaginable. At least that was the struggle I faced.

So this counsel to which I took an early offense was some sort of warning, an encouragement to resist the tendency to let Janene's intense and debilitating plight take me down with her.

As excruciatingly unsettling as it was, and still is, to preside over her physical, spiritual, and mental suffering, I have to be vigilant with self-care and enjoy the remarkably good health and meaningful life that is mine. Every day I try to embrace a spirit of gratitude for the blessing and joy of my life, so that I in turn can make good on my promise to care for Janene until she is freed from this extraordinary bondage.

The other disturbing bit of advice came from my sister-in-law, herself a 40-year veteran of nursing care for our elderly and demented population. She had teamed with my brother as Director of Nursing and Administrator for senior and assisted living centers for decades. She had accompanied hundreds, perhaps thousands, on the last leg of life's journey. After listening to me report Janene's transition from home to memory care living, without hesitation she responded, *"You now have your own life to live."*

I was raised to absorb marital teachings like "the two shall become one flesh," "'til death us do part," or again, "in sickness and in health." All the traditional wedding-vow language was not only familiar to me, it was part of my worldview and informed my relationship with Janene for decades before dementia made its claim on our marriage.

So it is little wonder that these cryptic statements of truth motivated by love for me and decades of exposure to one of life's most debilitating diseases took me by surprise. What eventually helped me navigate these unfamiliar waters is the uncommon notion of "differentiation."

Here is Edwin Friedman's definition of the concept in *A Failure of Nerve:*

Differentiation is the lifelong process of striving to define and express oneself, while at the same time staying connected in relationships of trust and significance. It is charting one's own way by means of our own internal guidance system, and considering the expectations and needs of our stakeholders.[1]

So this "both/and" approach in place of my all too common "either/or," "black and white" perspective was helpful and made sense to me in light of the ongoing conundrum to redefine what it meant to be a good husband now, under these unusual circumstances. I don't need to visit Janene every day. And, I also want to stay connected to her in spite of the profound limitations she now has to appreciate or understand.

It took 150-plus visits to New Dawn Memory Care at 2000 South Blackhawk and well over two years for me to deeply apply this concept of differentiation to my relationship with Janene under these painfully unique conditions. I can enter her mysteriously small world with empathy and kindness while at the same time enjoy the rich and rewarding life I am living. I am committed to taking good care of her *and* taking good care of myself too. And to state the obvious, if I am not guardian of my own well-being and next season of my life, how will I be able to execute on my pledge to Janene?

But it requires daily and hourly, perhaps even minute by minute, vigilance to live with joy and gratitude in the life

I now have without Janene's companionship, with the full knowledge that life for her is now lived in Cottage C, room C-3, and in the dining room three times a day. She no longer reads. She no longer recognizes any family member but me. She is without language. Her RN and MBA degrees lie dormant. Her body is but a shell of what it used to be. I, on the other hand, am writing this reflection at 37,000 feet en route home after a deeply rewarding and invigorating consult with an executive team in Florida. And frankly, on most days I am filled with both grief and gratitude. It's not "all good" as some of my friends advise. But it is all true.

And tomorrow I will eat lunch with Janene. It will be heartbreaking once again. But I have found a way not to cry in front of her. We will hold hands. Maybe I'll cut her meat to help her manage eating more easily. She will want to go back to bed right after lunch. I'll tuck her in under that familiar bedspread. She will get a big hug from me, and a kiss on the forehead. She always chuckles when I say my final, "I love you, Janene." Most of the time I make it to the car before the tears flow.

So I'm living my own life, the one that is now profoundly different than Janene's and the one we used to live together well. And I will stay connected to her in whatever primitive means she is now able to absorb. That's all we have left.

Well, not quite all.

There is that spiritual, mystical bond that is embedded in our relationship and in those long, piercing, wordless, soul-searching, intimate gazes we hold with one another that defy explanation. But that's another topic.

I am grateful for my own "internal guidance system." It has served me well, even before Janene's decline started years ago. There is much to be grateful for in this strangely undefined, almost married, almost single, sometimes deeply lonely, suspended, incomplete life I am now living. Three daughters who deeply love and support me, old and new friends, rewarding work, exceptional health, hiking, camping, hunting, fishing, biking, travel, spiritual fulfillment… the list goes on and on.

My life is flourishing, and Janene's is ebbing away.

Surely ours was a "relationship of trust and significance" for nearly 50 years. I will always honor that fact. Those memories I hold dear. She is still a stakeholder in my life with a dramatically particular set of needs that I intend to meet to the best of my ability and with God's help.

Charting my own way will not mean abandoning Janene. Rather, charting my own way means I am determined to honor Janene to the utmost, by living unreservedly and completely into her final message to me, "Take a larger way."

RESOURCES

Monet Moment

1. Westheider, Ortrud (editor), Michael Philipp (editor), Christoph Heinrich (editor). 2019. *Claude Monet: The Truth of Nature.* Co-organized by the Denver Art Museum and the Museum Barberini, Potsdam. Prestel.
2. Ibid.
3. Palmer, Parker. (April 27, 2014) "Standing in the Tragic Gap." www.couragerenewal.org (podcast)

My Anniversary

1. Frankl, Victor. (1959) *Man's Search for Meaning.* Boston: Beacon Press.
2. Sittser, Jerry. (2004) *A Grace Disguised.* Grand Rapids, Michigan: Zondervan.

Grim Reality

1. Charlie Rose Brain Series. (February 23, 2012) "Degenerative Diseases: A panel of neurologists examine Alzheimer's disease and Frontotemporal dementia."

Forgiveness

1. Lamott, Anne. (1999) *Traveling Mercies: Some Thoughts on Faith.* New York: Pantheon Books.
2. *Farther Along.* Old Gospel song of disputed origin.
3. *Bible.* Matthew 18:21,22 NIV
4. Author unknown.

Loneliness and Solitude

1. Hadas, Rachel. (2011) *Strange Relation: A Memoir of Marriage, Dementia, and Poetry.* Philadelphia: Paul Dry Books.
2. Vanier, Jean. (1998) *Becoming Human.* Canada.
3. Tillich, Paul. (1963) *The Eternal Now.* New York: Scribner.
4. Presley, Elvis. (1965) "So Close, and Yet So Far (from Paradise)." *Harum Scarum* soundtrack. Writers Joy Byers, Joy Johnston. Kobalt Music.
5. Tillich, *The Eternal Now.*
6. Ibid.
7. Five lines of "The Invitation" from The Invitation by Oriah. Copyright ©1999 by Oriah Mountain Dreamer. Used by permission of HarperCollins Publishers.

"My Heart Breaks with Yours"
1. O'Neill, Rob, Right Reverend Episcopal Bishop of Colorado. Used with permission.
2. McNamara, William. (1991) *The Human Adventure: The Art of Contemplative Living*. Element Books.

Zucchini Muffins
1. Frankl, Victor (1959) *Man's Search for Meaning*. Boston: Beacon Press.
2. Wiesel, Elie. (2006) *Night* from *The Night Trilogy: Night, Dawn, Day*. Translated from French by Marion Wiesel. New York: Hill and Wang.
3. Santayana, George. "The young man who has not wept is a savage, and the old man who will not laugh is a fool." Source unknown.

Holidays Without Her
1. Dickinson, Emily. From letters to Susan Gilbert. Source unknown.
2. Gilbert, Elizabeth. (October 2018) The TED interview "Elizabeth Gilbert shows up for…everything."
3. Pack, Arthur. (1989) *We Called it Ghost Ranch*. Abiquiú, New Mexico: Ghost Ranch Conference Center.
4. Whyte, David. (2015) *Consolations: The Solace, Nourishment and Underlying Meaning of Everyday Words*. Langley, Washington: Many Rivers Press.

Pleasant Places
1. *Bible.* Psalm 16:6 NIV
2. Whyte, David. (2015) *Consolations: The Solace, Nourishment and Underlying Meaning of Everyday Words.* Langley, Washington: Many Rivers Press.

Providence
1. Wikipedia. Providence, Rhode Island.

Day by Day
1. Sandell-Berg, Carolina. (1865) Hymn *Day by Day (and with Each Passing Moment).*

Holy Ground
1. Popova, Maria. Brain Pickings blog.
2. Bowler, Kate. (2019) *Everything Happens for a Reason: And Other Lies I've Loved.* New York: Random House.
3. Davis, Geron. (1983) Hymn *We Are Standing on Holy Ground.*

Will She Know Me?
1. Schaeffer, Francis. (1968) *The God Who Is There.* Illinois: Downer's Grove: Intervarsity Press.

A Lopsided Closet
1. Tournier, Paul. (1968) *A Place for You: Psychology and Religion.* New York: HarperCollins.

My Gift on Her Birthday
1. Alighieri, Danté. (14th Century) "The Inferno." Part One of *The Divine Comedy*.
2. St. Paul. *Bible*. 11 Corinthians 4:16-18 NIV

A Stellar's Jay
1. Browning, Elizabeth Barrett. (19th century) Poem *Aurora Leigh*.
2. Jesus. *Bible* Matthew 16:18 NIV

Heartbroken and Openhearted
1. Palmer, Parker. April 27, 2014. Podcast "Standing in the Tragic Gap." www.couragerenewal.org
2. Rohr, Richard. (2013) *Yes, And...Daily Meditations*. Cincinnatti, Ohio: Franciscan Media.
3. Popova, Maria quoting Elizabeth Gilbert. (July 22, 2020) Brain Pickings blog. "Elizabeth Gilbert on Loss and Grief."
4. Ibid.

Radical Hope
1. Lear, Jonathan. (2008) *Radical Hope: Ethics in the Face of Cultural Devastation*. Cambridge, Massachusetts: First Harvard University Press.
2. Kiper, Dasha. (September 7, 2015) "Hope Is the Enemy" in *American Scholar*.
3. Tolkien, J.R.R. (2014) *The Children of Húrin*. Edited

by Christopher Tolkien. New York: HarperCollins

4. Hebrew Story. *Bible.* Hebrews 11:8 NIV

5. Frankl, Victor. (1946) *Man's Search for Meaning.* Boston: Beacon Press.

6. Lewis, C.S. Source unknown.

Sweet Lament

1. Morrison, Toni. (2007) *The Bluest Eye.* New York: Vintage reprint edition.

2. Wright, N.T. (March 29, 2020) *Time.* "Christianity Offers No Answers about Coronavirus. It's Not Supposed To."

3. Tafilowski, Ryan. (2020) Denver Institute for Faith and Work. "What Should We Do with Unresolved Pain?" https://bit.ly/2KawXei

4. Prophet Jeremiah. *Bible.* Lamentation 3:19-23 NIV

5. African-American Spiritual. "Nobody Knows the Trouble I've Seen"

Incarnation or Scar Tissue

1. Conroy, Pat. (2003) *My Losing Season: A Memoir.* New York: Bantam Books, Reprint edition

2. De Chardin, Teilhard. (1993) Attributed to Teilhard de Chardin in *The Joy of Kindness* by Robert J. Furey. New York: Crossroads Publishing.

For the Long Haul

1. Lamott, Anne. (2006) *Plan B: Further Thoughts on Faith*. New York: Riverhead Books, reprint edition.
2. Kolodiejchuk, Brian. (2009) *Mother Teresa, Come Be My Light: The Private Writings of the Saint of Calcutta*. New York: Doubleday Religion.
3. Gerberich, A.H. (1938) *The Brenneman History*.
4. Whyte, David. (2002) *Crossing the Unknown Sea: Work as a Pilgrimage of Identity*. New York: The Berkeley Publishing Group.
5. Popova, Maria. Brain Pickings blog

Ranch Road 1222

1. Phillips, Adam. (2013) *Missing Out: In Praise of the Unlived Life*. New York: Picador.
2. St. Paul. *Bible*. Romans 8:28 NIV

Stouthearted

1. Norris, Kathleen. (2010) *Acedia and Me: A Marriage, Monks, and a Writer's Life.* New York: Riverhead Books, reprint edition.
2. Ibid.

"Take a Larger Way"

1. Tolkien, J.R.R. (2012) *The Hobbit*. New York: Houghton Mifflin Harcourt
2. Eldredge, John. (1997) *Sacred Romance: Drawing*

Closer to the Heart of God. Nashville: Thomas Nelson.

3. Rohr, Richard. (May 27, 2018) Morning blog *Daily Meditations*. "Let Your Life Speak."

4. Enger, Leif. (2002) *Peace Like a River*. New York: Atlantic Monthly Press, Reprint edition.

Grief and Gratitude

1. Friedman, Edwin. (2017) *A Failure of Nerve: Leadership in the Age of the Quick Fix*. New York: Church Publishing; Revised edition

ACKNOWLEDGMENTS

CHRISTINE, RACHEL, AND LISA, this book would not have been birthed without your unwavering support and encouragement. You were both grieving the loss of your mother and standing by me each step of the way. Your strength and love have kept dementia from destroying our family.

Georgeann, you are the sister I always wanted and the best sister-in-law imaginable through the interminable ordeal with your sister. Your persevering love, resilient care, and spiritual encouragement in the face of each declining stage with Janene is truly inspiring. If she could, Janene would let you know how deeply she loves you and appreciates all you have done for me and for her over the last decade and more.

Thom and Mark, you two have mastered the art of friendship. I am the beneficiary of your extraordinary capacity to go the distance with a suffering comrade. Tragedy, tears, anguish—nothing scared you away.

You men in my Alzheimer's/dementia men's group—Larry, Tony, Bob, Bruce, Bill, Don, Ed—you have been and are superior traveling companions on this long and treacherous journey with Janene. I'm grateful for each one of you guys.

To my firm and gentle editors, Mary Beth Lagerborg and Kathy Groom, your insightful and skilled review of my fragmented first drafts improved this project immeasurably. Mary Beth, you were a skilled guide for me through uncharted territory.

Here is a heartfelt thank you to the cadre of family members and friends in Denver, in America, and around the world who cared and prayed for Janene and me over the years.

My family and I are indebted to Bruce Miller and Jennifer Merrilees, at the University of California at San Francisco Center for Memory and Aging, for your definitive diagnostic work. Your team ushered us into the next chapter of Janene's illness and did so with extraordinary compassion, understanding, and professionalism. You were tender-hearted messengers of the most difficult news. Thank you.

And Janene, you fought the disease so courageously for so long, and then left me with your final request to "take a larger way." This book is my best effort to honor your message. For all of who you are and what you have done for me I will be forever grateful. I had no idea a person could miss another for so long and as deeply as I miss you.

ABOUT THE AUTHOR

JAY BRENNEMAN invests his professional life in personal and leadership development as an executive coach and family business advisor while residing in Denver. He holds a degree in Psychology from the University of Texas and Master of Social Work from the University of Denver. Jay and Janene have been married for more than 50 years and have three daughters living in Aspen and San Francisco. www.alargerway.com

Made in the USA
Las Vegas, NV
16 June 2021